# The Exhibition of Archaeological Finds of The People's Republic of China

Text Provided by The Organization
Committee of The Exhibition of Archaeological Finds of
The People's Republic of China

Calligraphy by KUO MO-JO
Vice Chairman of the Standing Committee of the
National People's Congress of the People's Republic of China
President of the Academy of Sciences of China

Exhibition dates in the United States:

NATIONAL GALLERY OF ART
Washington
December 13, 1974-March 30, 1975

THE NELSON GALLERY-ATKINS MUSEUM
Kansas City, Missouri
April 20-June 8, 1975

ASIAN ART MUSEUM OF SAN FRANCISCO
THE AVERY BRUNDAGE COLLECTION
San Francisco, California
June 28-August 28, 1975

Photographs courtesy The People's Republic of China

Cover: F84 Bronze chariots, horses and warriors unearthed at Wuwei (detail)

Front inside cover: F64 The central chamber of Liu Sheng's tomb during excavation (detail)

Back inside cover: F3 Panpo site under excavation (detail)

# FOREWORD

China is a country with a long history. The forefathers of the Chinese people, through ages of hard work, created a splendid civilization and left behind a rich store of ancient relics. Since the founding of the People's Republic of China, archaeological work, guided by Chairman Mao's policy of "making the past serve the present," has made marked progress. Surveys and excavations have been carried out at many important sites and ancient tombs in various parts of the country, bringing to light enormous quantities of cultural relics, the preservation of which has been given close attention.

The specimens shown in the Exhibition of Archaeological Finds of the People's Republic of China represent only part of those discovered since 1949 and include some of the latest finds during the Great Proletarian Cultural Revolution. Ranging from the fossil skull of the Lantian Man who lived some 600,000 years ago to 14th century relics of the Yuan dynasty, they indicate the general development of history and culture in ancient China. We hope that the Exhibition will contribute to the promotion of understanding and friendship between the people of China and other countries.

# CONTENTS

## PHOTOGRAPHS

Books and periodicals on archaeology and cultural relics published in the People's Republic of China Map of China showing Archaeological Sites mentioned in the Exhibition

## AUXILIARY EXHIBITS*

F1    The Former Imperial Palaces in Peking. (photo)

F2    Anchi Bridge of the Sui Dynasty at Chaohsien, Hopei. (photo)

F3    Panpo site under excavation, Sian, Shensi. (photo)

F4    The tomb of Liu Sheng, Prince Ching of Chungshan of Western Han dynasty at Mancheng, Hopei, under excavation. (photo)

F5 Chronological Table of the Chinese Dynasties

*Primitive Society*    c. 600,000 – 4,000 yrs. ago

*Slave Society*    c. 21st Century – 475 BC
Hsia    c. 21st – 16th Century BC
Shang    c. 16th – 11th Century BC
Western Chou    c. 11th Century – 770 BC
Spring and Autumn Period    770 – 476 BC

*Feudal Society*    475 BC – AD 1840
Warring States Period    475 – 221 BC
Chin    221 – 207 BC
Western Han    206 BC – AD 24
Eastern Han    AD 25 – 220
The Three Kingdoms    AD 220 – 265
Western Tsin    AD 265 – 316
Eastern Tsin    AD 317 – 420
Southern and Northern Dynasties    AD 420 – 589
Sui    AD 581 – 618
Tang    AD 618 – 907
Five Dynasties    AD 907 – 960
Sung    AD 960 – 1279
Liao    AD 916 – 1125
Kin    AD 1115 – 1234
Yuan    AD 1271 – 1368
Ming    AD 1368 – 1644
Ching    AD 1644 – 1840

(Down to the 20th year of the rein of Emperor Taokuang)

* Photographs and documentations, denoted by F1, F2, etc.

# PRIMITIVE SOCIETY
(c. 600,000 – 4,000 years ago)

China is one of the countries in the world possessing a rich store of human fossils. From times immemorial, the forefathers of the Chinese people inhabited, labored and multiplied on her vast land.

Like other peoples over the world, the Chinese have passed through various stages of social development: the classless primitive communal society, the slave society and the feudal society.

As a result of continued discoveries of human fossils and cultural relics since the founding of the People's Republic of China, it is now possible to link up various important stages of the evolution of mankind.

We now have fossils of the Yuanmou Man who lived about one million years ago, of the Lantian Man who lived about 600,000 years ago, and of the Peking Man who lived about 400,000-500,000 years ago. All three retain certain primitive physical features.

Of the period about 200,000 to 100,000 years ago, we have fossils of the Mapa Man, the Changyang Man and the Tingtsun Man, who through a long period of manual labor acquired physical features approaching those of modern man.

Of the period about 50,000 to 10,000 years ago, we have the fossils of the Liuchiang Man, the Tzeyang Man and the Upper Cave Man, whose physical features are similar to those of modern man. The society by then had gradually entered a period of the matrilineal communes.

It took quite a long time for the matrilineal communes to reach full development after their appearance. About 7,000 to 6,000 years ago many large and small matrilineal tribes were scattered over the vast expanse of China, leaving rich cultural relics to posterity. Distributed along the middle reaches of the Yellow River are mainly remains of the Yangshao culture, with the Panpo village site as a typical example of this primitive culture. Of a relatively later date was the Kansu Yangshao culture along the upper Yellow River. Both the Yangshao and Kansu Yangshao belong to the neolithic culture, with painted pottery as the main feature.

About 5,000 to 4,000 years ago, the matrilineal tribes along the Yellow and Yangtze Rivers gradually entered upon a period of patrilineal communes. The cultural remains of this period are the Lungshan and Chichia cultures along the Yellow River, and the Chuchialing and Chinglienkang cultures along the Yangtze.

During the final stage of primitive society, as a result of the growth of the productive forces and a surplus of products, private ownership and differentiation between the poor and the rich arose, giving rise to classes. With the disintegration of the primitive society about 4,000 years ago, China entered upon the slave society.

## I Excavations of the Sites of Lantian Man and Peking Man
(c. 600,000 – 400,000 years ago)

Fossils of a type of human being were discovered in 1963 and 1964 at Lantian in Shensi province and named the Lantian Man. He is slightly earlier than the Peking Man, having lived approximately 600,000 years ago.

Since the founding of the People's Republic of China in 1949, more fossils of the Peking Man, who lived 400,000-500,000 years ago, stone tools he used and evidence of his use of fire have been discovered at the world-famous Peking Man site of Choukoutien on the outskirts of Peking.

Both the Lantian Man and the Peking Man, who lived in the early Paleolithic Period, were able to fashion and use simple stone tools, to hunt, fish and gather wild fruits and edible plants so as to carry on a primitive human life.

## Exhibits

**1 Skull and lower jaw of Lantian Man.** (model)

Cranium: Unearthed in 1964 at Kungwangling village, Lantian, Shensi.

Lower jaw: Unearthed in 1963 at Chenchiawo village, Lantian, Shensi.

Both belonged to the same type of human being of the female sex. The cranium had a large and heavy supraorbital ridge and rather low and flat forehead. The cranium wall was very thick with a low vault and small cranial capacity. Lantian Man lived in the mid-Pleistocene geological age, his cultural age being the early phase of the Paleolithic Period dating from some 600,000 years ago. The physiological and morphological features and the stratification of Lantian Man are comparable in general to those of the Java Man. The discovery of Lantian Man enlarged our knowledge of the distribution of early man and provided additional valuable material for paleoanthropological study.

**2 Bust of Lantian Man.** (restoration)

Made in 1972 by the Institute of Vertebrate Paleontology and Paleoanthropology of the Chinese Academy of Sciences.

**3 Pointed tool of quartzite.** (used by Lantian Man) (reproduction)

Length 17.5 cm

Unearthed in 1965 at Kungwangling village, Lantian, Shensi.

Fashioned by chipping a pebble.

**4 Scraper of vein quartz.** (used by Lantian Man) (reproduction)

Length 2.8 cm

Unearthed in 1965 at Kungwangling village, Lantian, Shensi.

Sharp edge at one end.

**5 Skull of Peking Man.** (model)

Unearthed in 1966 at Locality I of Choukoutien, Peking.

It belonged to a male comprising of frontal and occipital bones. The discovery of the fossils (representing 40 individuals) of Peking Man and other relics is of great importance to paleoanthropological studies. The skull of Peking Man is characterized by its low flat forehead and heavy brow ridge. The cranium wall is rather thick and cranial capacity smaller than that of modern man though larger than that of Lantian Man, with protruding jaw and large teeth but apparently chinless. Peking Man lived in the middle phase of the mid-Pleistocene age, about 400,000-500,000 years ago.

**6 Lower jaw of Peking Man.** (model)

Unearthed in 1959 at Locality I of Choukoutien, Peking.

Belonged to an aged female.

**7 Stone hammer.** (used by Peking Man)

Length 8.2 cm

Unearthed in 1966 at Locality I of Choukoutien, Peking.

With traces of being used on both sides.

**8 Flint scraper.** (used by Peking Man)

Length 13.2 cm

Unearthed in 1966 at Locality I of Choukoutien, Peking.

With traces of being used on both edges.

**9 Flint scraper.** (used by Peking Man)

Length 8.6 cm

Unearthed in 1966 at Locality I of Choukoutien, Peking.

Edge chipped on both sides.

**10 Scraper of vein quartz.** (used by Peking Man)

Length 4.5 cm

Unearthed in 1966 at Locality I of Choukoutien, Peking.

**11 Burnt earth.** (evidence of use of fire by Peking Man)

Length 24 cm

Unearthed in 1966 at Locality I of Choukoutien, Peking.

Brownish purple, with cinder and ash.

**12 Burnt bone.** (evidence of use of fire by Peking Man)

Length 11 cm

Unearthed in 1966 at Locality I of Choukoutien, Peking.

Blackened fragment of charred jaw bone of a deer.

**13 Burnt stone.** (evidence of use of fire by Peking Man)

Length 8.5 cm

Unearthed in 1966 at Locality I of Choukoutien, Peking.

Dark bluish grey, burnt cracks on stone surface.

The burnt earth, bones and stones as well as piles of ash found in the cave inhabited by Peking Man testify to his use and control of fire — a great discovery and important event in the history of mankind.

## Auxiliary Exhibits

F6 Important sites of primitive society in China. (map)

F7 Where the lower jaw of Lantian Man was found. (photo)

F8 Where the cranium of Lantian Man was found. (photo)

F9 Cranium of Lantian Man. (photo)

F10 Lower jaw of Lantian Man. (photo)

F11 Site of Peking Man at Choukoutien. (photo)

F12 Site of Peking Man under excavation in 1966. (photo)

F13 Cranium of Peking Man discovered in 1966. (photo)

## II Yangshao Culture Site at Panpo Village, Sian, Shensi Province
(c. 6,000 years ago)

The remains of a neolithic village discovered at Panpo in the eastern suburbs of Sian, Shensi province, cover an area of approximately 50,000 square meters. About 10,000 square meters were excavated between 1954 and 1957. The excavations uncovered dwelling foundations, kiln sites and a public cemetery, yielding nearly 10,000 artifacts. A specimen of charcoal gave a $C14$ date of $4115 \pm 110$ BC, and a carbonized fruit stone unearthed from the late stratified deposits gave a $C14$ date of $3635 \pm 105$ BC. ($C14$ dates are based on the $5730 \pm 40$ half-life).

The villagers practiced primitive farming and livestock breeding as well as hunting and fishing at this time. They had also mastered weaving, sewing and pottery making, and were able to paint their pottery with lively decorative patterns. The rims of some of the painted pottery are incised with over 20 different marks, simply and neatly executed. This indicates that people at that time probably recorded events by making marks and signs, which may be closely connected with the start of writing in China.

Yangshao culture is one of the neolithic cultures of Chinese primitive society. It is so called because it was first discovered at Yangshao village in Mienchih, Honan province.

## Exhibits

**14 Stone axe.**

Length 12 cm

Farm tool, black, polished, oval in section.

**15 Stone chisel.**

Length 8 cm

Craft tool, black, polished, narrow rectangular in section.

**16 Stone adze.**

Length 6 cm

Craft tool with cutting edge ground on one side, polished.

**17 Bone spade.**

Length 11 cm

Farm tool with flat straight cutting edge, polished.

**18 Bone chisel.**
Length 14 cm
Craft tool, well polished all over, with cutting edge ground on both sides, slightly curved.

**19 Bone harpoon head.**
Length 14.8 cm
Fishing tool, with cylindrical shaft and flat point barbed on both sides.

**20 Bone arrow head.**
Length 6.1 cm
Hunting tool.

**21 Bone hairpin.**
Length 16 cm
For keeping the hair knot in place.

**22 Bone needle.**
Length 16.5 cm
For needlework. One end sharpened and the other flat and perforated.

**23 Stone whorl.**
Diameter 3.8 cm
For spinning thread.

**24 Pottery bowl.** (with textile impressions on bottom)
Height 4 cm, diameter of mouth 13 cm
Food vessel of red pottery. The textile impressions on the bottom testify to the use of weaving at that time.

**25 Pottery bowl.** (with matting impressions on bottom)
Height 10.5 cm, diameter of mouth 24 cm
Food vessel of red pottery. The rim is painted outside with a wide ornamental band in brown and the bottom marked with matting impressions.

**26 Pottery jar with stippling.**
Height 11 cm
Container of red pottery, belly decorated with stippling.

**27 Pottery jar** with finger-nail impressions.
Height 15 cm
Container of red pottery, upper belly decorated with finger-nail impressions.

**28 Pottery amphora** with pointed bottom.
Height 43 cm
Water-filling container of red pottery, with narrow mouth, short neck and pointed bottom. The belly is flanked with two ears and its upper part decorated with fine cord impressions.

**29 Pottery basin** painted with human-mask design.
Height 17 cm, diameter of mouth 44.5 cm
Basin of red pottery, symmetrically painted inside with a pair of human masks and net-like designs in brown. The bottom is drilled with one hole, and the upper belly with five holes. The basin was placed on a funerary urn when unearthed.

**30 Pottery basin** painted with deer design.
Height 17 cm, diameter of mouth 42.8 cm
Red pottery. The interior is symmetrically painted with four deer in brown and the bottom drilled with a hole. The basin was placed on a funerary urn when unearthed.

**31 Pottery bowl** painted with triangle design.
Height 9 cm, diameter of mouth 14.5 cm
Food vessel of red pottery. The upper belly is painted with triangle and slanted line design in brown.

**32 Pottery jar** painted with triangle design.
Height 12.7 cm
Container of red pottery. The upper belly is painted with triangles in brown.

## Auxiliary Exhibits

F14 Model of the Panpo village site. (1:80)
F15 Panpo site during excavation. (photo)
F16 Panpo Museum. (photo)
F17 Use of the spinning whorl. (drawing)
F18 Restored stone axe and adze. (drawing)
F19 Marks on pot and potsherds. (2 photos)

## III Painted Pottery of the Kansu Yangshao Culture
(c. 4,000 years or more ago)

These painted pottery wares which belong to the late Neolithic Period are from the Kansu Yangshao culture discovered at different places in Kansu province on the upper Yellow River. $C$ 14 tests gave their dates as 2575 ± 100 BC, 2185 ± 100 BC and 2065 ± 100 BC. The painted pottery ware of the Kansu Yangshao culture, though handmade, is thin and even in wall and elegant in form. Hematite powder and manganese oxide were used as pigment. The beautiful decorative patterns harmonize with the shape of the vessel. Most of the patterns are geometrical, some with a blending of light and heavy lines, others with black and red in contrast. They evidence the remarkable artistic level of the craftsmen of the time.

## Exhibits

**33 Painted pottery waisted jar.**
Height 18.3 cm
Unearthed in 1958 at Lanchow, Kansu.
Container of red pottery. The rim is painted with zigzag design and outer surface with ornamental reticulations, bands, lines and circles in black.

**34** Painted pottery **tou** (stemmed bowl) with wave design.
Height 16.4 cm
Unearthed in 1958 at Lanchow, Kansu.
Food vessel of red pottery. The inside is painted with undulating design, the outside with ornamental waves and bands, all in black and brown.

**35 Pottery basin** painted with curved lines.
Height 9.5 cm, diameter of mouth 23 cm
Unearthed in 1966 at Lanchow, Kansu.
Food vessel of red pottery. The rim is painted with curved lines and dots interspersed with ornamental reticulations in dark brown. The outside of the upper belly is painted with wave design and the inside with ornamental crosses, dots, curved lines, circles and triangles.

**36 Painted pottery amphora** with flat bottom.
Height 38 cm
Unearthed in 1958 at Kanku, Kansu.
Container of red pottery. The body is painted in brown with an image of a human-headed, snake-bodied creature with open mouth, protruding eyes and outstretched arms, possibly the totem of a contemporary clan.

**37 Painted pottery vase** with four circles filled in with geometric pattern.
Height 49 cm
Unearthed in 1956 at Yungching, Kansu.
Container of red pottery. The upper belly is painted in brown with four circles filled in with geometric pattern.

## IV Chinglienkang Culture
(c. 5,000 years ago)

The Chinglienkang culture is one of the neolithic cultures of primitive society discovered after the founding of the People's Republic of China. Distributed mainly along the lower Yangtze and Huai Rivers, it was first discovered in 1951 at Chinglienkang, Huaian county, Kiangsu province. A specimen of wood unearthed at the site of Sungtse in Chingpu county near Shanghai gave a $C$ 14 date of 3395 ± 105 BC.

The people of those days engaged mainly in agriculture, cultivating paddy rice and raising pigs, dogs, sheep, cattle and other domestic animals. They also hunted and fished. Their painted pottery is unique in form and decoration.

## Exhibits

**38 Perforated stone axe.**
Length 15 cm
Unearthed in 1956 at Nanking, Kiangsu.
Farm tool, well polished all over, the perforation drilled from both sides.

**39 Stone knife** with seven holes.

Length 22.6 cm

Unearthed in 1956 at Nanking, Kiangsu.

Farm tool, polished, with perforations drilled from both sides. A typical specimen of Chinglienkang culture.

**40 Stone stepped adze.**

Length 17.3 cm

Unearthed in 1953 at Wuhsien, Kiangsu.

Craft tool, well polished all over, the upper section short and recessed for fastening with rope.

**41 Stone hoe.**

Length 13.5 cm

Unearthed in 1955 at Nanking, Kiangsu.

Farm tool, polished, with pecked perforation.

**42 Bone chisel.**

Length 16.3 cm

Unearthed in 1960 at Wukiang, Kiangsu.

Craft tool, with cutting edge well polished on both sides.

**43 Bone harpoon.**

Length 16.5 cm

Unearthed in 1960 at Wukiang, Kiangsu.

Fishing tool with sharpened point polished on both sides.

**44 Bone arrow head.**

Length 16 cm

Unearthed in 1960 at Wukiang, Kiangsu.

Hunting tool.

**45 Bone needle.**

Length 18.1 cm

Unearthed in 1960 at Wukiang, Kiangsu.

For needlework, with a hole at one end.

**46 Chueh** ring (penannular) of white jade.

Diameter 6.2 cm

Unearthed in 1956 at Nanking, Kiangsu.

Ear ornament.

**47 Huang** (half-ring) of green nephrite.

Length 12.6 cm

Unearthed in 1955 at Nanking, Kiangsu.

Pendant with perforations at both ends.

**48 Painted pottery bowl.**

Height 10 cm, diameter of mouth 18 cm

Unearthed in 1966 at Peihsien, Kiangsu.

Food vessel of red pottery. The body is white-coated and painted with red and black ornament of curved lines, whorls and dots.

**49 Painted pottery vase** with flower-petal design.

Height 19.5 cm

Unearthed in 1966 at Peihsien, Kiangsu.

Container of red pottery with narrow mouth and short neck. The upper belly is painted in black with white border, bringing out the flower-petal design.

**50 Pottery basin** painted with flower-petal design.

Height 16.5 cm, diameter of mouth 30.2 cm

Unearthed in 1966 at Peihsien, Kiangsu.

Food vessel of red pottery. Both rim and belly are white-coated and painted with petal design in black and brown.

**51 Pottery basin** painted with eight-point star design.

Height 18.5 cm, diameter of mouth 33.8 cm

Unearthed in 1963 at Peihsien, Kiangsu.

Food vessel of red pottery. The rim is white-coated and painted with red and black decoration. The upper belly is red-coated and painted with seven eight-point stars in white with black border.

## V Lungshan Culture in Shantung Province
(c. 4,000 years ago)

Lungshan culture is distributed along the middle and lower Yellow River and belongs to the late Neolithic Period. It is named after the small town of Lungshan in Licheng county, Shantung province, where it was first discovered in 1928.

The pottery wares on display are from those excavated at the site in Yaokuan village, Weifang, Shantung province, between 1959 and 1964. Mostly thrown on the potter's wheel, they are exquisite in form and show superb workmanship. The walls of some vessels are less than half a millimeter thick. Most have glossy black surfaces, indicating a fairly high level of craftsmanship.

## Exhibits

**52** Red pottery tripod **kuei** (pitcher).
Height 31.8 cm
Unearthed in 1960 at Weifang, Shantung.
Used for boiling water. Of red pottery mixed with fine sand, it has hollow legs.

**53** White pottery tripod **kuei** (pitcher).
Height 29.7 cm
Unearthed in 1960 at Weifang, Shantung.
Used for boiling water. Of white clay pottery mixed with fine sand, it has hollow legs.

**54** White pottery **ho** (kettle).
Height 31 cm
Unearthed in 1964 at Weifang, Shantung.
Used for boiling water. It is of white clay pottery mixed with fine sand. The vessel has a lid and its legs are hollow.

**55 Black pottery cup** with two ears.
Height 12.5 cm
Unearthed in 1960 at Weifang, Shantung.
Black pottery made of fine clay.

**56** Black pottery **tou** (stemmed cup) with thin body.
Height 16.3 cm
Unearthed in 1960 at Weifang, Shantung.
Black pottery food container made of fine clay. The body is egg-shell thin, the cup separable from its long stem.

**57** Black pottery tripod **ting**.
Height 15 cm
Unearthed in 1960 at Weifang, Shantung.
Black pottery cooking vessel made of fine clay with three legs in the shape of bird-head.

**58 Black pottery stemmed plate.**
Height 18.7 cm, diameter 43.8
Unearthed in 1960 at Weifang, Shantung.
Black pottery food container made of fine clay with flat bottom and high circular foot bearing two symmetrical perforations.

## SLAVE SOCIETY
(21st century – 476 BC)

China is one of the countries in the world whose civilizations developed very early. She has a recorded history of nearly four thousand years. The Hsia, Shang and Western Chou dynasties and the Spring and Autumn Period covered the approximately sixteen hundred years of the slave society.

In slave society, the slave-owning class appropriated to itself not only all the means of production, but the person of the slave as well. The slave-owners used slaves extensively in agricultural and handicraft production, exploiting and driving them most cruelly. The facts of history show that it was the slaves who, with their wisdom and labor, developed production and created a splendid civilization.

The founding of the Hsia dynasty (21st — 16th century BC) marked the beginning of China's slave society. The slave system further developed in Shang and Western Chou. During the Spring and Autumn Period the slave system gradually declined as a result of slave revolts and the emergence of the new landlord class. Embryonic feudalism grew within the body of slave society.

After the founding of the People's Republic of China, Chinese archaeological workers made investigations on the problem of Hsia dynasty culture, and new fruitful research has been done in the cultures of the Shang and Western Chou dynasties and the Spring and Autumn Period.

Shang was the name of an ancient tribe that inhabited the lower reaches of the Yellow River. In the 16th century BC Tang, the king of Shang, defeated Chieh, the king of Hsia, and founded the Shang dynasty. The slave system further developed in China. Agriculture was the main productive work, using the nine squares (**ching tien**) system in which land was divided into plots in the pattern of the Chinese character 井 "ching" (meaning a well), and allotted by the Shang ruler as fiefs to various slave-owning aristocrats, with slaves forced to till the land. Farm implements were mainly of wood, stone, or shell, but bronze tools were also coming into use. Crops included foxtail millet, broomcorn millet, wheat, rice, mulberry and hemp. The fermentation of wine was prevalent, indicating that agriculture was fairly well developed by that time.

The making of bronze vessels was the main handicraft of Shang times. Bronze is an alloy using tin to alloy copper, and bronze metallurgy was an important invention made by the slaves of Shang. In later Shang dynasty work in bronze reached a peak, the products showing fine skill and exquisite form. Among Shang bronzes are some huge vessels such as the **szu-mu-wu** ritual cauldron weighing 875 kilograms, demonstrating the slaves' artistic talent and advanced craftsmanship in bronze in such early times.

An outstanding achievement in ceramic technique of the period was the use of high-temperature firing to produce white clay pottery with pure white body, and proto-porcelain. Other handicrafts such as the carving of jade, stone and bone, and weaving, also showed considerable progress.

As a result of the independence of handicrafts from other production and the emergence of commerce and formation of state, cities became separated from the countryside. Remains discovered at Chengchow show the existence of an important city in the early Shang dynasty, while the Yin ruins at Anyang indicate the existence of an ancient capital of later Shang period there. Oracle bone inscriptions unearthed at the Yin ruins reveal well-developed forms of ancient Chinese writing.

Though the slaves created the Shang dynasty culture, yet the slave-owners used them as so many articulate tools, and when their owners died many of them were entombed as sacrificial objects.

Serious social crisis near the end of the Shang dynasty gave King Wu of Chou an opportunity to launch an expedition against Shang rule and, in a battle at Muyeh (present-day Chihsien county, Honan province), armed slaves in the Shang army mutinied, causing the Shang dynasty's collapse.

## VI   Shang Dynasty Site at Chengchow, Honan Province
(16th – 11th century BC)

Shang dynasty remains excavated at Chengchow, Honan province, in 1950 cover an area of 25 square kilometers, and excavations in subsequent years have revealed large quantities of cultural relics. Remains of ceramic workshops, bronze foundries, bone carving workshops and rammed-earth walls were found in addition to dwellings and tombs. The site is an important archaeological discovery made since the founding of the People's Republic of China.

The bronze vessels unearthed at Chengchow are smaller in size, thin walled and simply decorated, displaying the technical features of early Shang bronzes.

Pottery moulds for casting bronze, crucibles for refining ore, and bits of charcoal were found in the ruins of a bronze foundry. Analysis of a bronze wine vessel unearthed here shows the following composition: copper, 91.29%; tin, 7.1%; lead, 1.12% — indicating that the slaves of that time had mastered the technique of making bronze.

Proto-porcelain, forerunner of later Chinese porcelain wares, was also found in the ruins at Chengchow.

From the ruins of handicraft workshops and unearthed relics it is apparent that there was already in Shang times a fairly fine division of labor in handicraft production.

The thick, rammed earth walls enclosed fairly concentrated dwellings. In the tombs of the slave-owners were found coffins encased in a wooden sarcophagus and many burial accessories such as carved bone and ivory objects, bronze vessels, jade and pottery.

In some were found the skeletons of immolated slaves. Many slaves, however, were thrown into rubbish pits, like cattle, when they died.

## Exhibits

**59** Bronze **Ko** with whorl design.
Length 20.3 cm
Unearthed in 1954 at Chengchow, Honan.
The **Ko** (halberd) was evolved out of the stone sickle. It was used in fighting. The wooden shaft was rotted away. One side of the butt end is ornamented with whorl design; the other bears the clan insignia.

**60 Bronze spear head.**
Length 18.5 cm
Unearthed in 1954 at Chengchow, Honan.
The socket for fitting the shaft is oval shaped.

**61 Bronze arrow head.**
Length 6.7 cm
Unearthed in 1953 at Chengchow, Honan.
Barbed and mid-ridged for easy penetration, it is hard to extract.

**62 Bronze arrow head.**
Length 6.5 cm
Unearthed in 1954 in Chengchow, Honan.
Also barbed and mid-ridged.

**63 Bronze knife.**
Length 25.6 cm
Unearthed in 1954 at Chengchow, Honan.

**64 Dark green nephrite ko** (halberd).
Length 38 cm

Unearthed in 1955 at Chengchow, Honan.
For ceremonial use only. The tang has four groups of incised parallel lines. The original long handle has rotted away.

**65 Bone arrow head.**
Length 9.5 cm
Unearthed in 1955 at Chengchow, Honan.

**66 Bone pi (spatula).**
Length 11 cm
Unearthed in 1954 at Chengchow, Honan.
Craft tool.

**67 Bone comb.**
Length 10.1 cm
Unearthed in 1954 at Chengchow, Honan.
Horizontal and slanting lines are incised on the middle of one side. It has 13 teeth.

**68 Bone hairpin.**
Length 15.3 cm
Unearthed in 1955 at Chengchow, Honan.
For keeping the hair knot in place.

**69 Animal bone,** raw material for the manufacture of bone artifacts.
Length 14 cm
Unearthed in 1955 at Chengchow, Honan.
A section of the thigh bone of an ox, sawed off for making bone artifacts.

**70 Bronze lei** with animal-mask design.
Height 25 cm
Unearthed in 1955 at Chengchow, Honan.
Wine vessel with three groups of animal-mask designs on belly. There are three cruciform openings on the circular foot rim and three frog or tortoise designs on the neck. These designs are probably clan names, and are the earliest bronze inscription yet discovered.

**71 Bronze tripod chia** with animal-mask design.
Height 22 cm
Unearthed in 1955 at Chengchow, Honan.

Wine vessel with round bottom and three triagonal hollow legs. The belly is decorated with three groups of animal-mask designs.

**72 Bronze tripod ting** with animal-mask design.
Height 19 cm
Unearthed in 1955 at Chengchow, Honan.
Cooking vessel with round bottom and three cone-shaped hollow legs. The belly is decorated with three groups of animal-mask designs.

**73 Bronze pan** with **kuei** dragon design.
Height 10.5 cm, diameter of mouth 30 cm
Unearthed in 1955 at Chengchow, Honan.
Food vessel with **kuei** dragon design on the belly and three cruciform openings on the circular foot rim. The **kuei** is an artist's expression of a mythical monster.

**74 Bronze tsun** with animal-mask design.
Height 24.9 cm
Unearthed in 1954 at Chengchow, Honan.
Wine vessel with three ox heads on its shoulder and animal-mask designs on the belly. The circular foot rim has three openings.

**75 Bronze tripod li** with **kuei** dragon design.
Height 16.5 cm
Unearthed in 1955 at Chengchow, Honan.
Cooking vessel with conical solid legs and a band of **kuei** dragon design around the lower neck.

**76 Bronze ku** with animal-mask design.
Height 18 cm
Unearthed in 1965 at Chengchow, Honan.
Wine vessel decorated with animal-mask design on the lower belly. Its circular stand has three cruciform openings.

**77 Bronze chueh** with animal-mask design.
Height 17.2 cm
Unearthed in 1965 at Chengchow, Honan.
A flat-bottomed wine vessel with three triagonal pointed legs. Its belly is decorated with two groups of animal-mask designs.

**78** Large-mouthed **tsun** (wine container) of proto-porcelain.

Height 28.2 cm

Unearthed in 1965 at Chengchow, Honan.

Made of kaolin, body of greyish yellow hue, impressed with geometric patterns on the shoulder and long, slender lines on the belly. Yellowish green glaze on surface and mouth of the ware and massed translucent deep green glaze on the inner and outer surfaces. Fired at 1,200° C., it has a low rate of water absorption. It is the earliest proto-porcelain so far found in China.

The chemical composition of the body and glaze of Shang proto-porcelain unearthed at Chengchow is as follows:

**79** Pottery **yen.**

Height 40 cm

Unearthed in 1953 at Chengchow, Honan.

Vessel for steaming food. It is grey pottery mixed with sand, with three pouched legs, ornamented with thick cord design on its surface.

**80** Pottery **tsun.**

Height 34.5 cm

Unearthed in 1954 at Chengchow, Honan.

Water vessel of grey pottery. Its surface is decorated with slightly raised lines and thick cord patterns.

## Auxiliary Exhibits

F20 Distribution of Shang dynasty sites at Chengchow. (sketch map)

F21 Remains of building foundation. (photo)

F22 Vestiges of rammed-earth wall. (photo)

F23 Remains of bronze foundry. (photo)

F24 Inscription on bronze **lei** with animal-mask design. (rubbing)

## VII  The Yin Ruins at Anyang, Honan Province
(14th – 11th century BC)

The famous Yin ruins at Anyang, the remains of an ancient Shang capital after the 14th century BC, represent the civilization of the late Shang dynasty. Since the founding of the People's Republic of China, many excavations have been made at the site and a wealth of artifacts unearthed, including inscribed bronze vessels and oracle bones. In 1950 at Wukuan village, the large tomb of a slave-owner was excavated, 8.4 meters underground, occupying 340 square meters (the longest distance from north to south is 45 meters, and the longest distance from east to west is 12 meters). The skeletons of 79 immolated slaves were found, as well as bronze, gold, jade, pottery and shell objects, and also traces of silk fabrics on a bronze plate, surviving due to being impregnated with cuprous oxide. These finds provide important specimens for research into the slave society of the Shang dynasty.

## Exhibits

**81** Bronze **yu** with the inscription "Pei Kan (?)".

12 century BC

Height including the handle 29 cm

Unearthed in 1950 from the large tomb at Wukuan village, Anyang, Honan.

Wine vessel with the two-character inscription "Pei Kan (?)", probably the name of a clan, on the inside bottom.

**82** Bronze **kuei** with the inscription "Pei Kan (?) Ko".

12th Century BC

Height 14.3 cm, diameter of mouth 20.7 cm

Unearthed in 1950 from the large tomb at Wukuan village, Anyang, Honan.

Food vessel with the three-character inscription "Pei Kan (?) Ko" on the inside bottom.

**83** Bronze tripod **ting** with the inscription "Fu Chi".

11th century BC
Height 21.7 cm
Unearthed in 1950 at Anyang, Honan.
Cooking vessel with the two-character inscription "Fu Chi" on the inside wall, denoting that it was made for offering sacrifice to Fu Chi (Fu, father; Chi, name) by his son.

**84 Bronze tripod chia** with the inscription "Mu Ya".
12th century BC
Height 30.8 cm
Unearthed in 1959 at Anyang, Honan.
Wine vessel with the two-character inscription "Mu Ya", probably the name of a person, on the inside bottom.

**85 Inscription on ox shoulder blade.**
14th century BC
Length 40.5 cm
Unearthed in 1971 at Anyang, Honan.
Two lines of 18 characters are inscribed on one side, recording a sacrificial offering by a slave-owner to his ancestors.

Slave-owners of the Shang dynasty consulted the oracle on all important occasions. The material used for this purpose was mainly shoulder blades of oxen or plastrons of tortoises. Deep, round dents were drilled on one side of the shell or bone and these were heated until cracks appeared on the reverse side. The cracks were then taken as the oracle's voice prophesying good or evil. The process of consulting the oracle and its "reply" were inscribed along the sides. More than 5,000 different characters of fairly well-developed forms have been discovered among these inscriptions, which make up the earliest written language yet discovered in China, and form an important basis in studying the history and culture of the Shang dynasty.

**86 Inscription on ox shoulder blade.**
14th century BC
Length 37 cm
Unearthed in 1971 at Anyang, Honan.

On one side is an inscription of 25 words divided into three lines. It records the offering of sacrifice by a slave-owner to his ancestors.

## Auxiliary Exhibits

F25 Tomb of a slave-owner at Wukuan village, Anyang. (photo of model)

F26 Inscription of **bronze yu:** "Pei Kan (?)". (rubbing)

F27 Inscription of **bronze kuei:** "Pei Kan (?) Ko". (rubbing)

F28 Inscription of **bronze tripod ting:** "Fu Chi". (rubbing)

F29 Inscription of **bronze chia:** "Mu Ya". (rubbing)

F30 Inscribed ox shoulder blades **in situ.** (photo)

F31 & 32 Inscriptions on ox shoulder blades. (rubbings, 2 pieces)

F33 & 34 Inscriptions on ox shoulder blades. (enlarged, 2 pieces)

## VIII   Shang Dynasty Bronzes from Shansi, Anhwei and Hunan Provinces
(12th – 11th century BC)

Since the founding of the People's Republic of China, bronze vessels of the Shang dynasty have been found in Anhwei, Hunan, Hupeh, Kiangsi, Liaoning and other provinces.

Those exhibited here are only a part of the bronze articles of the late Shang dynasty unearthed in Shansi, Anhwei and Hunan provinces. The casting of bronze had reached a high level of perfection in China by that time. By using the piece-mould technique, the modeling was generally dignified and pompous, while some pieces seem bizarre and original. Good examples are the bronze **kuang** (wine vessel) with dragon design and the owl-shaped bronze **yu** (wine vessel) unearthed at Shih-lou, Shansi. Decorative motifs often consist of animal masks, dragon and phoenix designs. Realism was occasionally used, as in the rectangular bronze

**ting** (cooking vessel) with human-mask design. The bronze vessels of Shang and the succeeding Chou dynasty take an important place in the art history of the world.

## Exhibits

**87 Owl-shaped bronze yu**
11th century BC
Height 19.7 cm
Unearthed in 1957 at Shihlou, Shansi.
Wine vessel in the shape of two owls back to back, with a loop in the form of an animal mask on each side.

**88 Bronze kuang** with dragon design.
11th century BC
Length 41.5 cm
Unearthed in 1959 at Shihlou, Shansi.
Dragon-shaped wine vessel. A complete dragon is cast in relief on the lid. Around it are several small dragons, while on the two sides are crocodile designs. The vessel itself is in the shape of a snarling, swimming dragon. It is an exquisite work of art.

**89** Bronze **tsun** with animal-mask design.
12th-11th century BC
Height 47 cm
Unearthed in 1957 at Funan, Anhwei.
Wine vessel with three sacrificial animal heads on its shoulder; on its belly are three groups of large animal-mask designs with thunder and cloud patterns between. On the foot rim are four symmetrical cruciform openings. It is exquisitely made.

**90** Bronze tripod **chia** with animal-mask design.
12th century BC
Height 55.3 cm
Unearthed in 1965 at Feihsi, Anhwei.
Wine vessel with flat bottom and three pointed legs. Its belly is adorned with animal-mask design.

**91** Bronze rectangular **ting** with human-mask design.

11th century BC
Height 38.7 cm
Unearthed in 1959 at Ninghsiang, Hunan.
Cooking vessel. The four sides of its belly are decorated each with a human mask in relief. The masks on the front and back are different in size from those on the left and right, but in facial expression and features they are the same. On the inside is the inscription "Ta Ho", likely the name of a clan.

**92** Bronze square **tsun** with animal-mask decoration.
11th century BC
Height 53.8 cm
Unearthed in 1963 at Changning, Hunan.
Wine vessel with figure with animal head and bird body on each of its four shoulders and four ox heads in between. The four sides are decorated with animal-mask and **kuei** dragon patterns.

## Auxiliary Exhibits

F35 Dragon design of bronze **kuang.** (rubbing)
F36 Inscription on bronze rectangular **ting** with human-mask design. (rubbing)

# Western Chou Dynasty
## (11th century – 770 BC)

Chou was the name of a tribe that lived on the loess plateau along the Wei River in ancient times. After overthrowing Shang rule, King Wu of Chou set up a state of the slave system centered in the capitals Feng and Hao in modern Shensi province. By instituting vassal states and a patriarchal and hierarchic system during the early Western Chou dynasty, a whole network of slave-owning regimes was established.

Western Chou was an age when the slave system further developed in China. In agriculture, the nine squares (**ching tien**) system still prevailed and the method of fallow land was adopted. Handicrafts and commerce further developed. All principal towns had workshops for the casting of bronze articles of daily use for the nobility as well as weapons. Many ritual vessels were also cast for use in ancestral sacrifices and for recording military achievements and decrees of the king; some of these had fairly lengthy inscriptions.

It was the slaves who created this prospering economy and splendid culture; however the slaves themselves had no political rights at all. Five slaves were equivalent in value to a horse plus a roll of silk. Their life was insecure to the degree that they could be entombed alive or killed as sacrificial objects.

As a result of sharp social contradictions toward the end of the Western Chou dynasty, King Yu was killed in 771 BC and the dynasty came to an end. The following year King Ping, the son of King Yu, moved his capital eastward to Loyi (the present Loyang), and this period came to be known in Chinese history as the Eastern Chou dynasty. From then began the Spring and Autumn Period.

## IX Western Chou Bronzes from Chichia Village, Fufeng, Shensi Province
### (10th – 9th century BC)

Two hoards of Western Chou bronzes were discovered in 1960 and 1963 at Chichia village, Fufeng

county. Some 39 articles including a bronze wine vessel bearing the seal script "Chi Fu" were excavated at one site while half a dozen articles including another bronze wine vessel with the inscription "Jih Chi" were found at the other. These two vessels represent different styles. The one marked "Jih Chi" is a good specimen of early Chou bronzes. It is heavy but finely modeled and elaborately decorated with animal masks as the main motif. The other inscribed "Chi Fu" is typical of those of the later period, with only ribbon design or stylized animal pattern. Bronze vessels of this period usually bear long inscriptions. The Chi Fu vessel has an inscription of 57 characters, recording how one powerful slave-owner called Tung Chung awarded four families of slaves to Chi Fu.

## Exhibits

**93** Bronze **Kuang** marked "Jih Chi".
10th century BC
Height 31.6 cm
Unearthed in 1963
Rectangular wine vessel with lid in the shape of a two-horned mythical animal. On the animal's back is an inverted animal mask and on each of the two sides of its neck a **kuei** dragon looking backwards. The front, right and left sides of the body are decorated each with an animal-mask and bird pattern; at the back is a wide and flat animal tail. On the inside of the cover and on the body is an inscription of 20 characters saying that this bronze vessel was made for a slave-owner by the name of "Tien" for the purpose of offering sacrifices to his father "Chi" at his ancestral temple.

**94** Bronze square **tsun** marked "Jih Chi".
10th century BC
Height 29.5 cm
Unearthed in 1963
Wine vessel with an inscription of 20 characters on the inside bottom of the belly. Its context is the same as that on the bronze **kuang** marked "Jih Chi".

**95** Bronze square **yi** marked "Jih Chi".
10th century BC
Height 38.5 cm
Unearthed in 1963.
Food vessel with an inscription of 20 characters on the inside of the lid and on its body. Its context is the same as that of the bronze **kuang** marked "Jih Chi".

**96** Bronze **ho** with bird-shaped lid.
10th century BC
Height 38 cm
Unearthed in 1963.
Wine vessel with a flattened, oval belly, four legs and rectangular mouth. Besides its bird-shaped lid, it has an animal-shaped spout and a dragon-shaped handle.

**97** Bronze **hu** marked "Chi Fu".
10th-9th century BC
Height 59.4 cm
Unearthed in 1960
Wine vessel with lid and double handles in the shape of animal heads with a ring hanging from each mouth. It is decorated with curves and hooks, wave patterns as well as stylized animal-mask and **kuei** dragon designs interlocked with each other. Inside the vessel is an inscription of 57 characters recording how a big aristocrat Tung Chung awarded six bundles of aromatic herbs for ritual use, four slave families and 300 **jin** of bronze to Chi Fu at his western palace. This denotes that slaves, like herbs and other chattels could be given to others at will.

**98** Bronze **lei** with **kuei** dragon design.
10th-9th century BC
Height 46.1 cm
Unearthed in 1960.
Wine vessel with handles in the shape of animal heads with rings hanging from the mouth, and a circular foot rim. The shoulder is decorated with **kuei** dragon designs and whorl patterns, the belly with leaf-shaped lappets composed of **kuei** dragon designs.

**Auxiliary Exhibits**

F37 Inscription of bronze **hu**: "Chi Fu". (rubbing)
F38 Inscription of bronze square **yi**: "Jih Chi". (rubbing)

## X Western Chou Bronzes from Ketso Liaoning Province
(11th century BC)

In 1955 a number of early Western Chou bronzes were unearthed at Haitaoyingtze village in Ketso, Liaoning province, among them five bearing inscriptions. The most important one is the Yen Hou Yu (food vessel of the Marquis of Yen). The inscription on it is the same as those on the bronzes of the Marquis of Yen discovered near Peking. This shows that as early as the beginning of the Western Chou dynasty, what approximates the present-day Liaoning was already a fief conferred upon the Marquis of Yen by the King of Chou.

### Exhibits

**99** Bronze **kuei** marked "Yu Fu Kuei".
Height 16.7 cm, diameter of mouth 25 cm
Food vessel with wide mouth and circular foot rim. The outside of the mouth is decorated with animal heads and slightly raised lines and whorl patterns. The body is adorned with rhomboid forms and studded with nipple-like protrusions. On the inside bottom is the inscription "Yu Fu Kuei". Yu is the clan name, Kuei the personal name.

**100** Bronze **yu** marked "Shih Hsu".
Height including the handle 28.5 cm
Wine vessel with **kuei** dragon and phoenix designs. On the inside of the lid and the body are inscriptions of seven characters each, marking the ritual vessel as made for "Shih Hsu" in honor of his father "Jen".

F39 Inscription on bronze **kuei**: "Yu Fu Kuei". (rubbing)

F40 Inscription on bronze **yu**: "Shih Hsu". (rubbing)

## XI Western Chou Tombs at Tunhsi, Anhwei Province
(11th Century BC)

Over 300 funeral objects were excavated from three Western Chou tombs at Tunhsi in 1959 and 1965. They contained mainly bronzes and proto-porcelain wares. There have also been discoveries of proto-porcelain wares of this period at Changan in Shensi, Loyang in Honan, and Chenchiang in Kiangsu. Bronzes such as the **yu** (wine vessel) marked "Kung" are identical in design to those found in the Yellow River valley, but the bronze **kuei** (food vessel) decorated with stylized animal-mask design has certain local features.

### Exhibits

**101** Bronze yu marked "Kung".
Height including handle 23.5 cm
Unearthed in 1965.
Wine vessel. The front and back sides of the lid are decorated with a pair of phoenix designs and the handle adorned with an animal head at each end. Under the mouth rim are animal masks and **kuei** dragon designs, on the belly two pairs of phoenix patterns. On the inside of the lid and on the body are an inscription of ten characters each, indicating that this ritual vessel was made for "Kung" to honor his ancestors.

**102** Bronze **kuei** decorated with stylized animal-mask design.
Height 19.7 cm, diameter on mouth 27.2 cm
Unearthed in 1965.
Food vessel with special local features. It has ani-
mal-shaped ears, flat bottom and circular foot rim. The belly is decorated with stylized animal-mask design. This shows that metallurgy and the casting of bronzes were highly developed in the region of present-day Anhwei.

**103** Bronze **pan** with **kuei** dragon design.
Height 9.4 cm, diameter of mouth 31.6 cm
Unearthed in 1959.
Food vessel with ears and circular foot rim. The mouth and foot rim are each ornamented with a band of **kuei** dragon pattern.

**104 Proto-porcelain vase** with three handles.
Height 11 cm
Unearthed in 1965.
Both the shoulder and belly are decorated with slightly raised parallel lines. Apart from the circular foot rim, the inside and outside are covered with greenish yellow glaze.

**105 Proto-porcelain tsun** (wine vessel) with two handles.
Height 11.9 cm.
Unearthed in 1965.
The shoulders are marked with rhomboid pattern. Apart from the circular foot rim, the inside and outside are covered with greenish yellow glaze.

**106 Proto-porcelain vase** with two handles.
Height 15 cm
Unearthed in 1965.
The whole body is covered with slightly raised parallel lines. Apart from the circular foot rim, the inside and outside are covered with greenish yellow glaze.

### Auxiliary Exhibits

F41 Burial accessories in a Western Chou Tomb at Tunhsi **in situ**. (photo)

F42 Inscription of bronze **yu**: "Kung". (rubbing)

The Spring and Autumn Period was a time of transition from the slave system to feudalism in China. The royal house of Chou had declined while local vassal states, among them some dozen large ones, grew in power.

With the introduction of iron implements and ploughing with oxen, the social productive forces grew apace and the cultivated area was expanded. Private ownership of land arose, while the nine squares system gradually declined.

There followed further development in handicrafts and commerce. Bronze vessels were cast in neat and clean lines, the modeling becoming more expressive and elegant. Inlaying gold and copper was a new technical achievement of the time.

There were social unheavels and disintegration, with slaves and common people in continual insurrections and the newly emerging landlord class on the rise. In 594 BC the state of Lu began to levy taxes on private land, the earliest to legalize private land ownership. Other states followed suit. The newly emerging landlord class gradually seized political power and slave society declined.

## XII Bronzes of the Spring and Autumn Period from Anhwei and Shansi Provinces
(5th century BC)

The **pien chung** (a chime of bronze bells) on exhibit are from the famous tomb of the Marquis of Tsai at Shouhsien county, Anhwei province. The state of Tsai had already declined, yet burial accessories in this tomb were still most lavish. Large numbers of ceremonial bronze musical instruments and jade objects reveal the cruel exploitation of the slaves by the slave-owners. The bronze vessels discovered at the ruins of the state of Tsin of the Spring and Autumn Period at Houma, Shansi province, are massive with intricate designs. This was a transitional period in bronze casting from the style of the late Western Chou dynasty to that of the Warring States Period. The bronze rectangular

**hu** (wine vessel) and bronze **chein** (basin) shown here are typical of the Spring and Autumn Period.

## Exhibits

**107-115 Bronze pien chung** (a chime of bells) of the Marquis of Tsai. (9 pieces)
Height 16.6 - 28 cm
Unearthed in 1955 at Shouhsien, Anhwei.

A set of nine bells which, suspended from a rack, produce different notes when struck. They provide important material for the study of ancient Chinese music. There are inscriptions on the bells, some having as many as 82 characters and some with only three characters. The inscriptions record the relationship between the two states of Tsai and Chu.

**116 Bronze tripod ting** in the shape of a sacrificial animal.
Height 27.5 cm
Unearthed in 1959 at Shucheng, Anhwei.
Cooking vessel. The eyes are of turquoise; the right and left sides of the fore part of the body are each decorated with a coiled dragon in relief. Above the hind leg is a ridged tail.

**117 Bronze rectangular hu** with interlaced-dragon design.
Height 86.6 cm
Unearthed in 1961 at Houma, Shansi.
Rectangular wine vessel with animal-mask handles with dangling rings on the two sides. The four corners of the lid, neck and belly are respectively adorned with an animal, the belly being decorated with interlaced-dragon design. The top of the lid and foot rim have interlaced serpent and dragon openwork. The vessel is large yet well-proportioned, the ornamentation intricate yet orderly and meticulous. This is a salient feature of the bronzes of the Spring and Autumn Period. The vessel is a beautiful piece of art.

**118 Bronze chien** with interlaced-hydras design.
Height 36.8 cm, diameter of mouth 76 cm
Unearthed in 1961 at Houma, Shansi.

Water vessel with four animal-shaped handles. The neck and belly are adorned with three groups of interlaced-hydras design.

## Auxiliary Exhibit

F43 Inscription on the **bronze pien chung** of the Marquis of Tsai. (rubbing)

## FEUDAL SOCIETY
(475 BC – AD 1840)

Chinese feudal society, which began in 475 BC, continued for more than two thousand years through most of the dynasties in Chinese history (the Warring States, Chin, Han, the Three Kingdoms, the Western and Eastern Tsin, Southern and Northern Dynasties, Sui, Tang, the Five Dynasties, Sung, Liao, Kin, Yuan, Ming and Ching) right up to the Opium War in 1840. During this long course of history there was formed a unified, multi-national feudal country with a vast territory and a large population.

The peasant class and the landlord class were the two main classes in feudal society. Politically, the landlords dominated everything and economically they possessed most of the land. The peasants, who had no political power, suffered from economic exploitation. This ruthless political oppression and economic exploitation forced the peasants into numerous uprisings and wars unparalleled in scale in the history of the world.

A self-sufficient natural economy predominated in China's feudal society, known for its well-developed agriculture and handicraft industry. During this long period a splendid ancient civilization was created. The wealth of archaeological finds is eloquent proof that the people, and the people alone, are the motivating force in the making of world history.

After the Spring and Autumn Period came what is known in history as the period of Warring States in which the seven major vassal states — Chin, Chi, Chu, Yen, Han, Chao and Wei — carried on fierce wars of annexation among themselves.

The years of the Warring States were the formative period of the Chinese feudal society. The repeated uprisings by the slaves and the common people which had taken place during the late Spring and Autumn Period and the early Warring States Period gave the slave-owning aristocratic rule a heavy blow. The newly rising landlord class step by step seized political power and instituted social reforms. As a result of repeated fierce struggles, the feudal system began to be firmly established.

This period saw steady improvement in iron-smelting technique, with pig iron smelted at a high temperature of 1,250° C. for the making of iron tools. Production of iron implements in large quantities and their widespread use promoted the development of the productive forces. Water conservancy work made big headway. The Tuchiang-yen project constructed by the laboring people in Kuanhsien county, Szechuan province, for instance, is one of the famous water conservancy systems in ancient China. It has played a big role for the last 2,000 years. Handicraft goods such as silk and lacquer were superb. There was a rich variety of lacquerware of exquisite workmanship. Lacquer-wares with a thin wood base and sackcloth base were invented. There were also innovations in the technique of inlaying or gilding bronze with gold and silver.

## XIII   Surveys and Excavations of City Sites of Warring States Period
(4th century BC)

The capitals of the various vassal states during the period gradually developed into municipalities with relatively concentrated population. Chinese archaeological workers have, since the founding of the People's Republic of China, surveyed and ex-cavated important city sites of the period. These included the Second Capital of Yen at Yihsien county, Hopei province; the capital of Chao at Hantan, Hopei province; the capital of Chi at Lintze, Shantung province; the capitals of Cheng and later Han at Hsincheng, Honan province; the capital of Chu (known later as Chinan City) at Chiangling, Hupeh province; the ancient city of Tsin and later Wei at Houma, Shansi province; and the capital of Chin at Hsienyang, Shensi province. Many precious relics have been brought to light by these excavations.

The Second Capital of Yen, one of the famous cities of the Warring States Period, was situated southeast of Yihsien in Hopei. It was 8,300 meters from east to west and 4,000 meters from north to south. An ancient river course in the central part of the city ran south to north, separating it into an eastern and a western sector. The eastern sector was the center of activities for the inhabitants of the time. There were the palace quarters, handi-craft workshops for casting iron and making pot-tery, and the residential district. This sector was rich in cultural relics including production imple-ments, building materials, utensils for daily use and large quantities of coins and bronze weapons. Relics discovered in some of the foundations of the major buildings of the Second Capital of Yen are on display here.

## Exhibits

**119 Bronze knocker** ornamented with interlaced-hydras and phoenix design.

Length of animal mask 45.5 cm, diameter of ring 29 cm

Unearthed in 1966.

The knocker is fashioned in the shape of an ani-mal mask with a ring hanging from its mouth and a phoenix perched at the center of the forehead. Extended from the mouth is a semi-circular long-tongue polygonal in section, holding the flattened ring, the surface of which is interlaced with two hydras.

**120 Semi-cylindrical tile with cicada pattern.**
Length 54.5 cm
Unearthed in 1966.

**121 Semi-circular tile-end with animal-mask design.**
Diameter 23 cm, length 33.5 cm
Unearthed in 1964.

**122 Semi-circular tile-end with animal-mask design.**
Diameter 28 cm, length 14 cm
Unearthed in 1964.

## Auxiliary Exhibits

F44 Distribution of Surveyed and Excavated City Sites of the Warring States Period. (map)

F45 Remains of the Lienmatai at the Second Capital of Yen at Yihsien, Hopei. (photo)

F46 Remains of the capital of Chi at Lintze, Shantung. (photo)

F47 Remains of the capital of Chao at Hantan, Hopei. (photo)

F48 Remains of the ancient city at Houma, Shansi, during excavation. (photo)

F49 Remains of the capital of Chu (known later as Chinan city) at Chiangling, Hupeh. (photo)

F50 Plan of the remains of the Second Capital of Yen at Yihsien, Hopei.

## XIV  Iron-Casting Moulds from Hsinglung, Hopei Province
(4th century BC)

Iron tools were widely used in the Warring States Period. Since the founding of the People's Republic of China, large quantities of iron implements have been unearthed at the city sites and tombs of this period. In 1953, a hoard of 87 moulds, some open and some composite, for casting various kinds of iron tools was found in Hsinglung, Hopei province. The use of metal moulds increased the efficiency of making iron implements and made their production in large quantities possible. The use of cast iron and the invention of metal moulds represent a splendid achievement in the history of metallurgy of the laboring people in ancient China.

## Exhibits

**123 Iron mould and core for casting axe.** (3 pieces)
Length of mould 28.6 cm, length of core 21.9 cm
The mould is made up of two separate pieces joined by mortise and tenon. The core is wedge-shaped, with a tenon for insertion into the mortise of the mould. On the back of the mould pieces are arch-shaped handles. Analysis reveals the carbon content of the mould to be 4.45%, a typical specimen of "white cast iron". This is a relatively early object of pig iron discovered in China which bears out the fact that the technique of smelting pig iron at a temperature of 1,250° C. had already been mastered. One piece bears the inscription: "Right Granary", the name of the agricultural official in charge of the granaries in the state of Yen. This shows that the mould was made by government-owned handicraft workshops under the charge of the above-mentioned official.

**124 Iron mould for casting a pair of sickles.**
Length 32.5 cm
With arched handle on the back. The mould is inscribed with the words "Right Granary".

## Auxiliary Exhibits

F51 & 52 A pair of iron sickles. (recent castings)

F53 Iron axe. (recent casting)

F54 Inscription on the iron mould. (rubbing)

## XV  Chu Tombs at Chiangling, Hupeh Province
(5th century BC)

Ying, the capital of Chu during the Spring and Autumn and the Warring States Periods was what was later on known as Chinan city, in the present-day Chiangling county, Hupeh province. Three Chu tombs of the Warring States Period, with 900-odd objects including bronzes, jade ornaments, lacquerware and painted wood sculptures were excavated here in 1965-66. The large iron belt-hook with gold inlay on exhibition is a rare art object. The bronze sword with lozenge design also shows the high level in applied arts of the time.

## Exhibits

**125 & 126 Dragon-shaped jade ornaments.** (2 pieces)
Length 28 cm
Unearthed in 1965.
Made of green jade, used as pendants.

**127 Bronze sword** with lozenge design.
Length 60.8 cm
Unearthed in 1965.
The guard is inlaid with turquoise and the blade ornamented with "hidden" lozenge design. It is in perfect condition.

**128 Bronze tsun** (wine vessel) with stylized dragon design.
Height 17.1 cm
Unearthed in 1965.
The lid surface and vessel body are incised with stylized dragon design.

**129 Iron belt-hook** with gold inlay.
Length 46.3 cm
Unearthed in 1965.
The hook is fashioned in the shape of a dragon-head, the surface inlaid with gold bird and phoenix designs, while on the reverse side are two iron buttons inlaid with gold.

## Auxiliary Exhibits

F55 Design on the gold-inlaid iron belt-hook. (drawing)
F56 Stylized dragon design on **bronze tsun**. (drawing)

## XVI Pottery Moulds and Bronzes of Warring States Period from Shansi and Shantung Provinces
(5th century BC)

(1) Pottery moulds unearthed in Houma, Shansi.
Sites for casting bronzes were excavated at the ancient Hsintien remains in Houma, Shansi in 1959-60. The finds included melting ovens and crucibles as well as more than 30,000 pottery moulds — cores, outer moulds and models — for casting bronze vessels. The fine workmanship of these pottery moulds indicates improvement in the art of casting bronze to a new level. The bronzes were ornamented with interlaced-dragon or hydras designs as well as realistic hunting and feasting scenes. The tiger exhibited is a recent cast from an unearthed pottery mould.

## Exhibits

**130 Pottery mould** for casting the figure of a tiger. (3 pieces)
Length 18.5 cm
Unearthed in 1959.
The mould is composed of right and left pieces and a base. The tiger's head is held high and its tail curled as if in forward motion.

**131 Pottery model** for making mould of animal-head.
Height 10.9 cm
Unearthed in 1960.
The face is engraved with whorl, cloud and scale designs. The animal-head model consists of two parts which form a whole. The part shown is the left part.

**132 Pottery relief model** for making mould of animal-mask design.
Length 32.8 cm
Unearthed in 1960.
(2) Gold and silver inlay work of the Warring States Period unearthed in Shansi province.
Numerous gold and silver-inlaid bronze objects of

the Warring States Period were unearthed in Changchih, Hochin, Yungchi of Shansi province in 1954 and 1965. The skill of inlaying bronze ornaments with gold and silver required the cutting of shallow grooves for the design on the surface of the bronzes, setting the threads or thin segments of gold and silver in the grooves and then grinding to smoothness. This marked a new development by the Chinese working people in decorating bronze objects. The bronze **tou** (food vessel) inlaid with gold in **kuei** dragon design and the silver-inlaid ornaments on exhibition are among the best that have been found.

## Exhibits

**133 Bronze tou** inlaid with gold in **kuei** dragon design.
Height 19.2 cm
Unearthed in 1965 at Changchih, Shansi.
Food vessel decorated with stylized **kuei** dragon, lotus-petal, leaf-shaped lappet and triangular cloud patterns. It is meticulously made, with flowing lines.

**134 Bronze rim of vessel** inlaid with gold and silver.
Diameter 12 cm
Unearthed in 1954 at Hochin, Shansi.

**135 Bronze ornament** with silver inlay.
Diameter 21.3 cm
Unearthed in 1954 at Yungchi, Shansi.
The front end is in the shape of an animal head with a long neck. There is a rectangular socket at the rear. The whole piece is inlaid with silver.

(3) Bronze vessel unearthed in Shantung province.

**136 Bronze ewer** with eagle's head.
Height 47.5 cm
Unearthed in 1970 at Chucheng, Shantung.
The mouth of the vessel together with the lid form an eagle's head. The handle is looped to the lid with two rings. The eagle's beak opens as the con-

tents are poured. The shape is unique and it is intricately made.

## Auxiliary Exhibits

F57 Bronze tiger. (recent casting)
F58 Pottery model for making mould of animal head. (enlarged photo)

# 秦 Chin Dynasty
## (221 – 207 BC)

The Chin dynasty was a period in which a unified multi-national feudal country was formed in China. In keeping with the trend of historical development, Chin Shih Huang, the First Emperor of Chin (259 – 210 BC) defeated the six contemporary states and brought them under unified control in 221 BC. It was the first time in Chinese history that a unified feudal country under centralized authority had been founded.

Chin Shih Huang abolished the vassal system and introduced the system of establishing prefectures and counties. With a firm hand he suppressed the attempts of the slave-owning nobles to restore their lost power, introduced a uniform system of writing, effected the standardization of money, weights and measures, and had roads for couriers built all over the country. By carrying out political, economic and cultural reforms he helped to promote the development of the feudal system. Various sections of the walls built during the Warring States Period were rebuilt and linked up to form the world-famous Great Wall which extended from Lintao in the northwest to Liaotung in the northeast.

## XVII Cultural Relics of the Chin Dynasty from Shensi and Shantung Provinces
(3rd century BC)

The mausoleum of Chin Shih Huang is located at Lishan in present-day Lintung county, Shensi province. Chinese archaeological workers made a survey of the mausoleum and its surroundings in 1962 and found the foundation of its double enclosure walls fairly well preserved. The inner wall is 578 meters from east to west and 684.5 meters from north to south, the length of the circumference is 2,525 meters. The outer wall is 974.2 meters from east to west and 2,173 meters from north to south, the circumference is 6,294 meters. There was nothing left of the buildings above ground. The remnant earth mound today is 43 meters high. In recent years cultural relics have been discovered from time to time around the mound. The large squatting figure of a woman which is on display was unearthed near the mound of Chin Shih Huang.

Each state of the Warring States Period had its own script, and each varied in form and structure with the locality. The system of weights and measures was also in a state of chaos. After defeating the six other states, Chin Shih Huang ordered his Prime Minister Li Szu and others to standardize the forms of writing so that one script could be used throughout the country, to set up unified regulations for weights and measures and make standardized models inscribed with Chin Shih Huang's edict. The pottery measure on display was one of the standard measures made at this time.

## Exhibits

### 137 Pottery measure.
Height 9.4 cm, diameter of mouth 20.4 cm
Unearthed in 1963 at Tsouhsien, Shantung.
The body of the vessel is impressed with an edict of Chin Shih Huang in the 26th year of his reign (221 BC). It says in brief: The unification of the country was achieved by defeating the six other states in the 26th year of the reign of Chin Shih Huang. The people have settled down to a state of stability. The imperial title of Emperor is hereby proclaimed. The Prime Ministers Wei Chuang and Wang Wan are commissioned to unify the prevailing laws, weights and measures and all other systems which are in confusion.

### 138 Brick stamped with a hunting scene.
Length 47.5 cm
Unearthed in 1957 at Lintung, Shensi.
Each end has either a tenon or a mortise. One side of the brick is stamped with four sets of designs depicting mounted horsemen hunting with bows and arrows, with hounds chasing deer on a wooded hill.

### 139 Pottery figure of a squatting woman.
Height 64.5 cm
Unearthed in 1964 at Lintung, Shensi.

Figure of a woman squatting in upright position with hands on knees. She wears a gown with overlapping lapels, and a skirt. It is a masterpiece of sculpture by an unknown artist of ancient times.

## Auxiliary Exhibits

F59 Mausoleum of Chin Shih Huang at Lintung, Shensi. (plan and photo)
F60 Inscription on pottery measure. (rubbing)
F61 Hunting scene stamped on a brick. (rubbing)

The Han dynasty is divided into two periods, the Western Han (206 BC – AD 24) with its capital at Changan, and the Eastern Han (AD 25 – 220) with its capital at Loyang.

The large-scale peasant uprising led by Chen Sheng and Wu Kuang spurred the economic and cultural development of Western Han. Inheriting the institutions of the Chin dynasty, the Han dynasty was a period in which the unified, multi-national feudal country was consolidated and further developed. Improvement in farm technique and water conservancy work enlarged the area of cultivated land. The use of iron tools for farming was further popularized. Iron was also widely used in making weapons and utensils for daily use. Coal was already used for smelting iron during the Western Han period. In the early Eastern Han period hydraulic blowers were invented. Production of large quantities of iron tools resulted from this steady improvement in smelting and casting techniques.

The silk textile industry was highly developed during the Han dynasty. The brocades found in the Western Han tomb at Mawangtui, Changsha, had a profusion of colors, while the plain gauze was as thin as a cicada's wings. There was a great variety of lacquerware. The process of making these is complicated and involves a fine division of work. Commerce flourished. Excellent silks and lacquerware were sent abroad in large quantities. The capital at Changan was not only the political and cultural center of the Han dynasty but also an important commercial city of the Orient.

The invention of paper was an outstanding contribution by the laboring people of ancient China to the world's cultural development. The working people of the Western Han period began making paper from plant fibers. Drawing on the practical experiences of his predecessors, Tsai Lun of Eastern Han succeeded in making better quality, low-cost paper from tree bark, hemp, rags and old fish nets.

The paintings and sculpture which characterize the art of the Han dynasty are magnificent and full of vigor. Lacquerware, pottery and other applied arts were decorated with beautiful designs. The wall paintings and paintings on silk found in Han dynasty tombs of nobles usually took as their motifs the legends and stories of historical figures; they were elaborate in depiction and bold in color. Designs carved on stone or impressed on bricks, in low relief or incised lines included lively scenes from productive activities and daily life, expressing realism in the plastic arts of the time.

In the 2nd century BC, during the reign of Emperor Wu, Chang Chien (died in 114 BC) opened a route from Changan through Kansu and Sinkiang in northwestern China to Afghanistan, Iran and other countries. It was along this road that ancient China exported its silks to Iran and the eastern Mediterranean and to Europe, and was named by later historians the "Silk Road". Its opening promoted economic and cultural exchange between China and the West.

Late in the Eastern Han period class contradictions become very sharp as a result of the ruthless exploitation and oppression by the ruling class. The Yellow Turbans Uprising which took place in AD 184 shook the foundation of the Eastern Han dynasty.

## XVIII The Tombs of Liu Sheng, Prince Ching of Chungshan of the Western Han Dynasty, and of His Wife at Mancheng, Hopei Province (113 BC)

Two large tombs of the Western Han dynasty were excavated at Mancheng, Hopei province in 1968. They were the tombs of Liu Sheng, Prince Ching of Chungshan of the Western Han dynasty, and his wife Tou Wan. Liu Sheng was a half-brother of Emperor Wu and died in 113 BC. More than 2,800 objects were brought to light from the two tombs, which fully expose the extravagance and decadence of the feudal ruling class at that time and provide a great deal of important data for researches into the social history, art and culture of the period.

## Exhibits

**140 Bronze chuan** (water container) inscribed "Household of the Prince of Chungshan".
Height 13 cm, diameter of mouth 28.1 cm
Unearthed in 1968 from the tomb of Tou Wan at Mancheng, Hopei.
The inscription incised on the upper part of the vessel reads: "One bronze **chuan** of the household of the Prince of Chungshan. Capacity 3 **tou.** Weight 7 **chin** 13 **liang.** Serial number 59. Purchased by **lang-chung** (official title) Ting, at Hotung in the 4th month of the 34th year."

**141 Bronze hu** (wine vessel) with gold and silver inlay of bird script.
Height 40 cm
Unearthed in 1968 from the tomb of Tou Wan at Mancheng, Hopei.
The vessel has an inscription of 29 characters including those on the lid, which express the cravings of the feudal aristocracy for material enjoyment. The inscription reads in brief: Eat well and be merry, keep illness away and enjoy long life. The bird script is an ornamental fancy style of Chinese writing. This bronze **hu** is a rare specimen, indicating the remarkable craftsmanship on metal work of the Chinese laboring people at some 2,000 years ago.

**142 Bronze hu** (wine vessel) inlaid with gold and silver.
Height 59 cm
Unearthed in 1968 from Liu Sheng's tomb at Mancheng, Hopei.
It has coiled dragon pattern all over its body. On the bottom of the vessel is an inscription which says in brief: Wine vessel belonging to the kitchen of the Prince of Chu.

**143 Bronze lamp** in the form of a ram.
Height of ram 18.6 cm, length 23 cm
Unearthed in 1968 from Liu Sheng's tomb at Mancheng, Hopei.
The lamp is in the form of a kneeling ram. The

back can be raised on a hinge to rest against the ram's head forming an oil reservoir.

**144 Bronze lamp** with stand inscribed with "Household of Prince of Chungshan".

Height of lamp 5.2 cm, diameter of stand 22.1 cm
Unearthed in 1968 from Tou Wan's tomb at Mancheng, Hopei.

The lamp rests on a tray. It bears the inscription pointing out that this bronze lamp with handle and tray belonged to the household of the Prince of Chungshan.

**145 Bronze lamp** with shade.

Height 32.8 cm

Unearthed in 1968 from Liu Sheng's tomb at Mancheng, Hopei.

The lamp has a long hollow handle with one end leading to the round reservoir and the other leading to the bonnet of the shade, which has a sliding screen. When lighted the smoke is funneled into the hollow handle and down to the reservoir, keeping the air smoke-free.

**146 Bronze Poshan** censer supported by a human figure mounted on beast.

Height 32.4 cm

Unearthed in 1968 from Tou Wan's tomb at Mancheng, Hopei.

The censer is supported on the upraised palm of a figure mounted on a beast. The cover is openwork in the shape of a mountain top covered with clouds and interspersed with human figures and mythical monsters.

**147 Jade suit** sewn with gold thread, shroud for Tou Wan, wife of Prince Ching of Chungshan.

Length 172 cm

Unearthed in 1968 from Tou Wan's tomb at Mancheng, Hopei.

Jade clothes sewn with gold thread were burial suits for the top members of the aristocracy. In accordance with rank, jade shrouds were divided into three categories, whether sewn with gold, silver, or copper thread. Tou Wan's suit consists of 2,160 plates of jade held together with gold

wire passed through holes at the corners. In all, 700 grams of gold were used. When unearthed, the body had turned to dust and some of the jade plates and gold wires were broken. The suit has been repaired.

**148 Bronze headrest gilt** with gold and inlaid with jade.

Length 41.3 cm

Unearthed in 1968 from Tou Wan's tomb at Mancheng, Hopei.

**149 & 150 Jade huang** (crescent-shaped ritual object). (2 pieces)

Length of smaller one 13 cm, length of larger one 13.7 cm

Unearthed in 1968 from Tou Wan's tomb at Mancheng, Hopei.

They had been held one in each hand of the dead.

**151 Tou Wan's bronze seal.** (reproduction)

Dimension 2 cm, thickness 0.7 cm

Unearthed in 1968 from Tou Wan's tomb at Mancheng, Hopei.

On one side are the incised characters "Tou Wan"; on the other "Tou Chun-hsu" (an informal name). There is a rectangular perforation from one edge through to the other.

**152–157 Jade pi discs.** (6 pieces)

Diameter 14.1 cm – 21.2 cm

Unearthed in 1968 from Tou Wan's tomb at Mancheng, Hopei.

Used as ornaments. Eleven pieces were discovered distributed around the dead, close to the jade suit.

**158 Iron knife** with a hilt-ring bound with gold wire.

Length 25.7 cm

Unearthed in 1968 from Liu Sheng's tomb at Mancheng, Hopei.

Besides the gold-wire binding of the hilt-ring, the hilt has gold-inlay cloud designs.

**159 Bronze dagger.**

Length 28.1 cm

Unearthed in 1968 from Liu Sheng's tomb at Mancheng, Hopei.

**160 Bronze sword.**
Length 72.5 cm
Unearthed in 1968 from Liu Sheng's tomb at Mancheng, Hopei.
The sword remains but the original sheath has decayed, leaving only two pieces of jade ornaments.

**161 Bronze ko** (halberd) with gilt bird-shaped ornament.
Length 20 cm
Unearthed in 1968 from Liu Sheng's tomb at Mancheng, Hopei.
On the top middle part of the **ko** is a gilt cylindrical shaft finial with a bird figure on top.

**162 Gold acupuncture needle.**
Length 6.5 cm
Unearthed in 1968 from Liu Sheng's tomb at Mancheng, Hopei.
Acupuncture was a unique form of medical treatment employed by the working people of ancient China in their age-long struggle against illness. This form of treatment is extensively used in China today.

**163 Silver acupuncture needle.**
Length 7.1 cm
Unearthed in 1968 from Liu Sheng's tomb at Mancheng, Hopei.

**164 & 165 Bronze leopards** inlaid with gold. (2 pieces)
Height 3.5 cm
Unearthed in 1968 from Liu Sheng's tomb at Mancheng, Hopei.
Four were unearthed. All are inlaid with gold and set with silver prunus-blossom designs. The eyes are of bright crimson gems tinged with yellow.

**166 & 167 Bronze feet of vessel** in the shape of bears and birds. (2 pieces)
Height 11.4 cm & 11.7 cm

Unearthed in 1968 from Liu Sheng's tomb at Mancheng, Hopei.

**168 Pottery basin** painted with fish design.
Height 14.7 cm, diameter of mouth 55.5 cm
Unearthed in 1968 from Liu Sheng's tomb at Mancheng, Hopei.

## Auxiliary Exhibits

F62 Location of the Principality of Chungshan in the Western Han Dynasty. (sketch map)

F63 Plans and sections of the tombs of Liu Sheng and Tou Wan, with sketch plans showing their location.

F64 The central chamber of Liu Sheng's tomb during excavation. (photo)

F65 Southern side-chamber of Tou Wan's tomb. (photo)

F66 Northern side-chamber of Tou Wan's tomb. (photo)

F67 Stone doorway of back-chamber of Tou Wan's tomb. (photo)

F68 Gold and silver inlaid bird script on the bronze **hu.** (photo)

F69 Bronze lamp in form of a ram. (photo)

F70 Inscription on the bronze **chuan** showing that it belonged to the household of the Prince of Chungshan. (rubbing)

F71 Inscription on bronze lamp with stand showing that it belonged to the household of the Prince of Chungshan. (rubbing)

F72 Inscription on bronze **hu** inlaid with gold and silver. (rubbing)

F73 Impressions of Tou Wan's bronze seal.

F74 The jade suit of Tou Wan, wife of the Prince Ching of Chungstan as discovered. (photo)

## XIX Western Han Tombs at Shihchaishan, Chinning, Yunnan Province
(2nd – 1st century BC)

Between 1955 and 1960 some 40 tombs of the King of Tien of the Western Han dynasty and his family were unearthed at Shihchaishan, near Chinning county in Yunnan province. Nearly 5,000 objects were found. Among the finds were a gold seal with the inscription reading "Seal of the King of Tien", and bronze objects such as drums, cowrie-shell containers, production tools, household utensils, weapons, figurines and the **wu chu** coins. There were also iron implements and agate and carnelian ornaments. These new finds provide important information for the study of the social life and production of the various nationalities in China's Yunnan province in ancient times.

Emperor Wu of the Western Han dynasty appointed the Chief of the Tien tribes in the Tienchih area as the King of Tien and bestowed a gold seal on him. At that time the Tienchih area was under the jurisdiction of Yichou prefecture and the Tien people still retained the social forms of the slave society to a considerable extent. On the lid of one cowrie-container in the exhibition are cast slaves weaving under the supervision of a slave-owner. Among the finds are also a number of bronze articles decorated with animal figures of which oxen were most frequently used.

## Exhibits

**169 Bronze ploughshare.**
Length 30 cm
Unearthed in 1956.

**170 Bronze axe** ornamented with two birds.
Height 24 cm
Unearthed in 1956.

**171 Bronze mandarin duck.**
Height 11.2 cm
Unearthed in 1956.

**172 Bronze cowrie-container** decorated with a weaving scene on its lid.

Height 27.5 cm, diameter of bottom 30.9 cm
Unearthed in 1955.
Container for storing cowrie shells, which were used as currency. On the cover is cast a female slave-owner supervising nine female slaves weaving, with eight others in attendance.

**173 Bronze ornament** in the form of buffalo heads and bulls.
Width 11.2 cm
Unearthed in 1956.

**174 Bronze ornament** in the form of a boar struggling with two tigers.
Length 17.1 cm
Unearthed in 1956.

**175 Bronze deer.**
Height 15.6 cm
Unearthed in 1956.

**176 Bronze peacock.**
Height 14.4 cm
Unearthed in 1956.

**177–192 Agate and carnelian beads.** (16 pieces)
Length 1.1 cm — 7.3 cm
Unearthed in 1956.
A string of beads, some are cylindrical and others barrel-shaped, in a variety of bright colors such as deep red and pink.

**193–198 Agate and carnelian button-shaped ornaments.** (6 pieces)
Diameter 4.4 cm — 5.8 cm
Unearthed in 1956.
There are two holes on the back for threading. The colors vary from white to pink and red.

## Auxiliary Exhibits

F75 Design on the bronze axe ornamented with two birds. (drawing)
F76 Detail of weaving scene on bronze cowrie-container. (drawing)

F77 The bronze ornament in the form of buffalo heads and bulls. (enlarged photo)

F78 The bronze ornament in the form of a boar struggling with two tigers. (enlarged photo)

## XX Applied Arts of the Han Dynasty
(206 BC – AD 220)

Since the founding of the People's Republic of China, a great number of Han dynasty cultural relics have been found in various parts of the country. Many of them are exquisite pieces which testify to the fine workmanship of that period. The painted pottery horseman figurines of the Western Han dynasty, the wooden monkey and painted wooden unicorn of the Eastern Han dynasty are all lively in form and varied in posture.

Gold and silver inlay work was further developed in the Han dynasty. A rare piece is a bronze chariot ornament in the exhibition. Less than 30 cm long, it is skillfully inlaid with gold, silver and turquoise, which successfully creates four scenes of decorative patterns. The figures of the rare animals, birds and the hunters are all brought into relief by the use of exaggeration, and the ornament as a whole gives a sense of unity. It presents a vivid picture of Han dynasty nobles hunting. The inlaid gold and silver lines are delicate, some of hair's breadth, and the colors are resplendent. This shows a further development of the inlay work in the Han dynasty on the basis of the techniques of the Spring and Autumn and the Warring States Periods. It is an example of the creative ability and skillful workmanship of the Han dynasty artists.

## Exhibits

**199 & 200 Painted pottery horsemen.** (2 pieces)
2nd century BC
Height 65 cm & 68.5 cm
Unearthed in 1965 at Hsienyang, Shensi.
Two of the 4,000-odd painted pottery honor guard horsemen unearthed from the large Western Han tomb at Yangchiawan, Hsienyang city.

**201 Bronze fang** (square wine vessel) inlaid with gold in hydras design
2nd century BC
Height 61 cm
Unearthed in 1964 at Sian, Shensi.

**202 Silver-inlaid bronze tsun** (wine vessel) in the form of a sacrificial animal.
2nd century BC
Height 27.4 cm, length 41.8 cm
Unearthed in 1965 at Lienshui, Kiangsu.
The mouth of the animal is a spout, part of the back a hinged lid. The body is covered with inlaid silver in cloud pattern; the head, tail and lid surface are set with turquoise and the eyebrows inlaid with gold.

**203 Bronze chariot ornament** inlaid with gold and silver.
1st century BC
Length 26.5 cm
Unearthed in 1965 at Tinghsien, Hopei.
In the form of a bamboo stem, it is divided into four sections by slightly raised lines. The whole is covered with inlaid gold and silver patterns and studded with turquoise. It is an outstanding art piece reflecting certain aspects of social life during the Han dynasty as well as its legend.

Against the background of a mountainside with clouds, flowers and trees, the first section shows three persons on elephant back as well as winged figures, a dragon, a horse, a bear, rabbits, deer, storks, birds, tortoise and others. The second section shows a mounted hunter turning back to shoot at a tiger with bow and arrow, also a bear, a wild boar, wolf, deer, monkeys, goats, birds and others. The third section depicts a person on camel back and a winged figure, a tiger, bears, deer, storks and others, while on the fourth section there is a peacock singing and spreading its tail along with winged figures, bears, tigers, deer, wild geese, storks and other figures.

**204 Bronze tsun** (wine vessel) with gold and silver decoration.

26 BC (the 3rd year of Hoping)
Height 34.7 cm, diameter of mouth 65.5 cm
Unearthed in 1962 at Yuyu, Shansi.
The whole body is decorated with gold. In addition, there are two groups of animals gilded with silver. In the top group are tigers, rabbits, deer and sheep, while in the lower are elephants, deer, bears, camels and warriors. All are outlined with black ink and tinged with red. On the rim is the inscription: "Bronze **tsun** made for Hu Fu of Yincheng, Chuyang county. Weight 120 **jin**. Made in the third year of Hoping (26 BC)."

**205 Gilded bronze tsun** for warming wine.
26 BC (the 3rd year of Hoping)
Height 24.5 cm, diameter of mouth 23.4 cm
Unearthed in 1962 at Yuyu, Shansi.
The vessel is gilded with gold and decorated with bird and animal designs in relief. The inside is lacquered. On the inner side of the lid are **kuei** dragon and phoenix designs painted with ink. The inscription on the rim of the lid and the vessel reads: "Bronze **tsun** for warming wine, owned by Hu Fu of Chungling.
Weight 24 **jin**. Made in the third year of Hoping (26 BC). Serial No. 2."

**206 Painted pottery vase.**
1st century BC
Height 49.5 cm
Unearthed in 1957 at Loyang, Honan.

**207 Pottery model of a courtyard.**
1st century AD
Height 76 cm, width 93 cm
Unearthed in 1959 at Chengchow, Honan.
A courtyard with buildings on the four sides made of grey pottery. It consists of the main rooms, a storehouse, watch towers, gatehouse, kitchen, pigsty and privy. It is a model of a landlord's or a noble's courtyard.

**208 Painted wooden unicorn.**
2nd century AD
Height 38.5 cm, length 59 cm

Unearthed in 1959 at Wuwei, Kansu.
The figure is done in simple and clean-cut lines. It was covered with a white powder and then painted with vermilion, but most of these colors have peeled off. It was a burial object of a noble, supposed to ward off evil.

**209 Wooden monkey.**
2nd century AD
Height 32.5 cm
Unearthed in 1957 at Wuwei, Kansu.
The body was painted with red, black and white, but most of the color has peeled off.

**210 Pi** disc of green nephrite decorated with animal design and ring.
1st century AD
Height 30 cm
Unearthed in 1969 at Tinghsien, Hopei.
Ornament of some noble.

**211 Pi** disc of green nephrite decorated with hydras design.
1st century AD
Height 25.5 cm
Unearthed in 1959 at Tinghsien, Hopei.
Ornament of some noble.

**212–217 Pottery figures** of musicians and dancers. (6 pieces)
1st century AD
Height 15 cm-15.5 cm
Unearthed in 1965 at Loyang, Honan.
Three of the figures are musicians and the other three are dancers. They are painted with red, white and black.

## Auxiliary Exhibits

F79 Developed design on bronze chariot ornament inlaid with gold and silver. (enlarged drawings)
F80 Developed design on bronze **tsun** with gold and silver decoration. (drawing)
F81 Inscription on bronze **tsun** with gold and silver decoration. (rubbing)

F82 Design on gilded bronze **tsun** for warming wine. (rubbing)
F83 Inscription on gilded bronze **tsun** for warming wine. (rubbing)

## XXI Bronze Figurines, Chariots and Horses from Eastern Han Tomb in Wuwei, Kansu Province
(2d century AD)

In 1969 a large Eastern Han dynasty tomb was discovered at Leitai, Wuwei county in Kansu province. It contained over 220 pieces of cultural objects and 30,000 copper coins. Most outstanding is a complete cortège of bronze figurines of warriors, chariots and horses, which vividly depicts the pomp and splendor of the procession of the feudal nobles when they went about.

The 39 bronze horses unearthed from this tomb are spirited, vigorous and beautiful. They reflect a high level of bronze casting and sculpturing. A significant art treasure is a unique, lively horse of bronze in the exhibition, galloping with its head and tail high. To show that its speed is greater than that of a bird, the unknown craftsman placed its right hind hoof on a swallow in flight and its others in the air, while the flying swallow looks back in amazement. The artist skillfully balances the galloping horse by using the body of the swallow to enlarge the contact point of the horse on the ground. This masterpiece in ancient Chinese art is evidence of the artist's rich imagination and skillful workmanship in bronze casting and sculpturing.

### Exhibits

**218 Bronze galloping horse.**
Height 34.5 cm, length 45 cm

**219 & 220 Bronze horses.** (2 pieces)
Height 36.5 cm & 38 cm

**221 Bronze horseman.**
Height 39 cm

**222 Bronze horseman** armed with halberd.
Height 52.3 cm

**223 Bronze horseman** armed with spear.
Height 53 cm

**224–227 Bronze chariot** mounted with axe. (a chariot, a horse and two figurines)
Height of horse 40 cm, length of chariot 33 cm
This is the first chariot of the honor guard.

**228–231 Bronze yao** chariot. (a chariot, a horse and two figurines)
Height of horse 40 cm, height of chariot 43.5 cm
Chariot ridden by the nobility.

**232–234 Bronze chu cart.** (a cart, a horse and a figurine)
Height of horse 38 cm, length of cart 63 cm
Cart for carrying possessions of the nobility.

**235 Procession scene,** part of the wall-painting of an Eastern Han tomb. (copy)
170 x 327 cm
Discovered in 1971 at Anping, Hopei.

### Auxiliary Exhibit

F84 Bronze chariots, horses and warriors **unearthed** at Leitai, Wuwei. (photo)

両晋南北朝

# The Three Kingdoms, the Western and Eastern Tsin, and the Southern and Northern Dynasties
(AD 220 – 589)

In AD 220 the Eastern Han dynasty came to an end and the Three Kingdoms of Wei, Shu and Wu were established. After the period of the Three Kingdoms, which lasted 61 years, unity was finally achieved by the Western Tsin (AD 265 – 316). In AD 316 the Western Tsin was succeeded by the Eastern Tsin dynasty (AD 317 – 420). Following the Eastern Tsin, in the south, four dynasties reigned in succession. They were Sung, Chi, Liang and Chen. In the north, the founding of the Northern Wei dynasty (AD 386 – 534) unified most of north China. Later on Northern Wei was divided into Eastern and Western Wei which were then succeeded by Northern Chi and Northern Chou. From the end of the Eastern Tsin dynasty in AD 420 to the unification of China by the Sui dynasty in AD 589, the period of division of China into north and south, which lasted over 160 years, is known in history as the Southern and Northern Dynasties.

The period of the Western and Eastern Tsin and the Southern and Northern Dynasties marks a period of intermingling of the various nationalities of China. Working and living together for a long time, the people of various nationalities came to have closer economic and cultural contacts.

In the early period of the Eastern Han dynasty (1st century AD), Buddhism was introduced into China, and by the time of the Southern and Northern Dynasties it began to spread and flourish. In the Northern Dynasties a large number of Buddhist images were hewn on cliffsides, which created the splendid art of grotto temples.

Among the most famous of these are the caves at Yunkang at Tatung, Shansi province, Lungmen Grottos at Loyang, Honan province, and Maichishan Caves at Tienshui and the Mokao Caves at Tunhuang, both in Kansu province.

## XXII Ceramics of the Tsin and Southern and Northern Dynasties from Chekiang, Kiangsu and Honan Provinces
(AD 265 – 589)

Techniques for making celadon (proto-celadon stoneware) developed further in north and south China during the Western and Eastern Tsin, and the Southern and Northern Dynasties. They reached a high level of perfection both in form and glaze. The celadon pot with the head of a cock and the jar with four rings were popular shapes at the time. The eagle-shaped celadon vase on exhibit was a work of the Western Tsin dynasty. The form is unique and attractive. The yellow-glazed flat flask decorated with musicians and dancers, a work of the Northern Chi dynasty, is remarkable for its lifelike design and glossy glaze. At the neck of the flask is a pair of knobs for attaching a string for convenience in carrying.

## Exhibits

**236 Celadon jar** crowned with miniature buildings and human figures.
Western Tsin (latter half of 3rd century AD)
Height 46.6 cm
Unearthed in 1965 at Shaohsing, Chekiang.
The jar is crowned with a pavilion having a gate tower and four corner watch towers. On the first and second tiers are a total of 18 seated figures in kneeling position with arms crossed on their chests. Warriors and running animals are embossed on the belly of the jar. It portrays a type of stronghold built by the hereditary landlords south of the Yangtze River during the Western and Eastern Tsin dynasties. Celadon with greyish green glaze was generally fired at a temperature of 1,100°-1,200°C. The glaze contains one to three percent ferrous oxide and would produce greyish green color only when baked in reduction kiln atmosphere.

**237 Celadon vase** in the shape of an eagle.
Western Tsin (first half of 4th century AD)
Height 17 cm

Unearthed in 1964 at Nanking, Kiangsu.

On one side is a projecting eagle head; the wings are incised on the belly and two claws protrude from the lower fore part of the body, while at the back is a tail.

**238 Celadon lion-shaped vessel.**
Western Tsin (latter half of 3rd century AD)
Length 17.5 cm
Unearthed in 1966 at Tanyang, Kiangsu.

**239 Celadon pot** ornamented with the head of a cock.
Eastern Tsin (4th century AD)
Height 23.5 cm
Unearthed in 1967 at Yuyao, Chekiang.

With dragon-shaped handle and cock-head spout, it was a prevalent form of porcelain ware of Eastern Tsin dynasty.

**240 Celadon vase** with dish mouth and eight rings.
Southern Dynasties (first half of 6th century AD)
Height 26 cm
Unearthed in 1964 at Juian, Chekiang.
The body is decorated with lotus-petal lappets.

**241 Celadon jar with incised design.**
Northern Chi (latter half of 6th century AD)
Height 29 cm
Unearthed in 1958 at Puyang, Honan.

The shoulder and belly are incised with circular, tree and duck-shaped patterns. Celadon from the north.

**242 Yellowish green-glazed jar** with dark green splashes and four rings.
Northern Chi (latter half of 6th century AD)
Height 23.5 cm
Unearthed in 1958 at Puyang, Honan.

It has a fine, white base incised with acanthus and lotus-petal patterns.

**243 Yellow-glazed flat flask** decorated with musicians and dancers.
Northern Chi (latter half of 6th century AD)

Height 20.5 cm
Unearthed in 1971 at Anyang, Honan.

In the middle is a man on a lotus-shaped pedestal dancing to music provided by players on the **pipa** lute, cymbal (left) and flute, and another clapping (right). The decoration on the reverse side is the same.

## XXIII  Stone Sculpture of the Northern Dynasties from Shansi and Hopei Provinces
(AD 386 – 581)

The stone sculptures of the Northern Dynasties have great artistic merit. The well-known Yunkang caves at Tatung, Shansi, are a great artistic creation of the people of various nationalities in north China. The place is one of the treasure houses of China's ancient stone sculpture. The stone carved with dragons and tigers, and the one carved with musicians, dancers, dragons and tigers on display were unearthed at Tatung. Graceful in form and meticulous in carving, these two pieces were probably done at the same time as the sculptures of the Yunkang caves. They are typical examples of the smaller sculptures of the Northern Wei dynasty.

### Exhibits

**244 Stone carved with dragons and tigers.**
Northern Wei (5th century AD)
Height 16.5 cm, width 32 cm
Unearthed in 1966 at Tatung, Shansi.

The material is light grey sandstone. The upper part is drum-shaped with a lotus flower carved on top and a circular hole in the center, surrounded by dragons pacing over hilltops in high relief. The upper part rests on a square seat with low relief of leaf-scroll designs and musicians carved on the sides. It was discovered in the tomb of Szuma Chin-lung (died in AD 484) of Northern Wei.

**245 Stone carved with figures of musicians, dancers, dragons and tigers.**

Northern Wei (5th century AD)

Height 16.5 cm, width 32.6 cm

Unearthed in 1966 at Tatung, Shansi.

The material is light grey sandstone. The upper part is drum-shaped with a lotus flower carved on top and a circular hole in the center, surrounded by dragons pacing over hilltops in high relief. The upper part rests on a square seat with low relief of acanthus and cloud patterns, with musicians and dancers carved on the sides. At the four corners are four standing boys beating a drum, blowing the **piehli** horn, playing the **pipa** lute and dancing respectively. It was discovered in the tomb of Szuma Chin-lung (died in AD 484) of Northern Wei.

**246 Stone image of Sakyamuni in the act of preaching.**

Northern Chi (latter half of 6th century AD)

Height 72.6 cm

Unearthed in 1958 at Linchang, Hopei.

Sakyamuni is seated on a lotus throne under the Bodhi tree. Flanking him are his four disciples and two Bodhisattvas. On the top are eight apsarases and a celestial dragon. Beneath the lotus throne is a rectangular stone platform at the middle of which are two boys offering incense with an upheld censer. On each side is a guardian and a lion.

## Auxiliary Exhibit

F85 Details of the stones carved with dragons and tigers, and with figures of musicians, dancers, dragons and tigers. (rubbing)

## XXIV Han to Tang Dynasty Cultural Relics from Sinkiang Uighur Autonomous Region (1st – 7th century AD)

Since the founding of the People's Republic of China silk and woolen fabrics as well as cottons of the period between the Han and Tang dynasties have been found from time to time along the old Silk Road at Minfeng, Turfan and Pachu in China's Sinkiang Uighur Autonomous Region. Official and private documents, pottery figurines and remains of food were also discovered.

The decorative patterns of the fabrics are usually the traditional Han designs such as lozenges, clouds, animals, birds and flowers. There are also the decorative designs then prevalent in western Asia such as a pearl-bordered medallion and confronting birds — designs used for export. Some fabrics have both Han characters and popular western Asian patterns. These fabrics are historical evidence of the trade and friendly interchange between China and the central and western Asian countries. Ancient brocade is a fabric woven with intricate craftsmanship. In the exhibition is a brocade mitten of the Eastern Han dynasty interwoven with the Chinese characters: Yen Nien Yi Shou, meaning "May your years be prolonged and your longevity be increased". The brocade with tree pattern of the Northern Dynasties, the brocade of the Tang dynasty with flower-and-bird design, the brocade with motif of a drinking pair and the yellow gauze with motif of confronting birds dyed by wax-resist technique are rare specimens of this kind.

## Exhibits

**247 Brocade mitten with the characters: Yen Nien Yi Shou.**

Eastern Han (1st – 2nd century AD)

Length 24 cm

Unearthed in 1959 from a site at Niya, Minfeng county in Sinkiang.

Warp-patterned brocade in plain weave. Dark red, white, bright blue, fawn and brown silk threads were used in the pattern of birds and animals as well as the Han characters: Yen Nien Yi Shou, Ta Yi Tzu Sun (May your years be prolonged and your longevity be increased; may you be favoured with many descendants). To weave such brocade involves 75 heddles for guiding the warps.

**248 & 249 Woolen fabric with grape pattern.** (2 pieces)

Eastern Han (1st – 2nd century AD)

Length 22.5 cm & 26 cm

Unearthed in 1959 from a site at Niya, Minfeng county in Sinkiang.

Weft-patterned and densely woven.

**250 Woolen girdle.**

Eastern Han (1st – 2nd century AD)

Length 29 cm

Unearthed in 1959 from a site at Niya, Minfeng county in Sinkiang.

Weft-patterned stripes of red, yellow and purple double woolen threads.

**251 Yellow damask with lozenge pattern.**

Eastern Han (1st – 2nd century AD)

Length 24.5 cm

Unearthed in 1959 from a site at Niya, Minfeng county in Sinkiang.

Warp-patterned damask in plain weave.

**252 Brocade with tree pattern.**

Northern dynasties (6th century AD)

Length 20.5 cm

Unearthed in 1959 from Astana, Turfan county in Sinkiang.

Warp-patterned brocade in plain weave. Woven with dark red, light blue, green, light yellow and white silk threads.

**253 Blue woolen fabric** with pattern dyed by the wax-resist technique (batik)

Northern dynasties (5th century AD)

Length 11 cm

Unearthed in 1959 from Wuyulaike, Yutien county in Sinkiang.

**254 Brocade with flowers-and-birds design.**

Tang dynasty (8th century AD)

Length 38.2 cm

Unearthed in 1968 from Astana Turfan county in Sinkiang.

Brocade in twill weave. A multi-colored posy is woven with scarlet, white, green, yellow, blue and purple wefts on red background. Surrounding it are birds, hills and trees.

**255 Brocade with the motif of confronting birds.**

Tang dynasty (7th century AD)

Length 26 cm

Unearthed in 1969 from Astana, Turfan county in Sinkiang.

Warp twill, with yellow background. Woven with light yellow, red and white silk threads.

**256 Brocade with picture of a drinking pair.**

Tang dynasty (8th century AD)

Length 12.8 cm

Unearthed in 1969 from Astana, Turfan county in Sinkiang.

Warp twill, with yellow background. Woven with blue silk threads are two figures standing beside a wine cask and imbibing from drinking horns, surrounded with a pearled-border in blue color.

**257 Yellow gauze with design of confronting birds,** dyed by the wax-resist technique (batik).

Tang dynasty (8th century AD)

Length 57 cm

Unearthed in 1968 from Astana, Turfan county in Sinkiang.

**258 A Tang dynasty register of household and land allocation:** the household of Ning Ho-tsai, Kao-chang county.

AD 689 (the 1st year of Tsaichu, Tang dynasty)

29 cm x 82.3 cm

Unearthed in 1964 from Astana, Turfan county in Sinkiang.

It lists the family members of Ning Ho-tsai, a peasant of Kaochang county and the number of **mou** of land allocated to him. It proves that the even field system in force at the beginning of the Tang dynasty was also used in the Sinkiang area. A seal bearing the inscription: "Seal of Kaochang County" is imprinted at the connecting place in the document.

**259 Loan contract** signed by Pai Huai-lo as debtor. AD 670 (the 3rd year of Tsungchang, Tang dynasty) 29 cm x 43 cm

Unearthed in 1964 from Astana, Turfan county in Sinkiang.

Written on hemp paper, the contract records the borrowing by Pai Huai-lo of ten silver coins and the monthly interest of one coin, showing the exploitation in the form of usury at that time.

**260 Fried bread-roll.**

Tang dynasty (7th century AD)

Length 18 cm

Unearthed in 1960 from Astana, Turfan county in Sinkiang.

**261 & 262 Chiaotzu** (dumplings). (2 pieces)

Tang dynasty (7th century AD)

Length 5 cm & 6 cm

Unearthed in 1960 from Astana, Turfan county in Sinkiang.

**Chiaotzu** (dumplings) is a traditional food of the Han people.

**263 Silver Sassanian coin.**

Diameter 2.9 cm

Unearthed in 1967 from Astana, Turfan county in Sinkiang.

Coined by Chosroes II (early 7th century AD). It is material evidence of the friendly early exchanges between China and Iran.

## Auxiliary Exhibits

F86 The Ancient Silk Road. (sketch map)

F87 Site at Niya, Minfeng. (photo)

F88 Remains of the ancient Kaochang county at Turfan. (photo)

F89 Brocade with animal-head pattern. (photo in color)

F90 Brocade with **kuei** dragon design. (photo in color)

F91 Brocade with design of confronting ducks. (photo in color)

The founding of the Sui dynasty ended the confrontation between the Northern and Southern Dynasties and once more unified China as a feudal multi-national country. This was achieved on the basis of the intermingling of the people of various nationalities in north China and the economic development in both the north and the south. The unification under the Sui dynasty further developed China's economy and culture.

In AD 582 the Sui dynasty built a magnificent new capital named Tahsing City (modern Sian). The capital Changan of the Tang dynasty was built and expanded on the foundations of the older Tahsing. Between AD 605 and 610 the Sui government had a grand canal dug of more than 1,500 kilometers. Extending from Hangchow in the south to Chochun prefecture (present-day Peking) in the north, it became a trunk communication line and played a major role in the economic interflow and transportation between north and south China.

The Grand Canal, one of China's well-known giant ancient engineering projects, marks the great achievement of the Chinese working people of ancient times in the transformation of nature.

The Anchi Bridge across the Hsiao River in Chaohsien county, Hopei province, was designed by a craftsman named Li Chun of the Sui dynasty. It is the world's earliest open-spandrel arch bridge. Built of limestone blocks, it is 54 meters long, while the span of the arch is 37.37 meters. The road surface of the bridge is gently sloped, convenient for the passage of horses and carts. At each end of the main arch are two small arches which act as spillways when the river is in spate. They add to the bridge's beauty and grace. On the parapet stones are exquisite carvings. The bridge was praised at the time as a "long rainbow resting on the Hsiao River". It is an amazing engineering feat of the Chinese working people in ancient times and evidence of the high level of bridge construction at the time.

In handicrafts, the Sui dynasty made further progress in porcelain making. In addition to large-scale production of celadons (proto-celadon stoneware), white porcelain had come into existence in north

China. It is distinguished for its snow-white body and sparkling glaze. This was a new invention of the ancient Chinese working people which laid the foundation for the manufacture of the white porcelain by Hsing and Ting kilns in the Tang and Sung dynasties.

## XXV   Chang Sheng's Tomb of Sui Dynasty at Anyang, Honan Province
(AD 595)

In 1959 the tomb of Chang Sheng of the Sui dynasty was unearthed at Anyang in Honan province. Chang Sheng, a general, died in AD 594 and was buried in the same tomb as his wife the following year.

The burial accessories in the tomb numbered 192 items. Among the finds are pottery models of utensils and others, like houses, stoves, wells, rotatory mills and rollers, and also a set of pottery musicians, which gives a cross section of the social life of the time. The porcelains unearthed fall into three main groups — the white porcelain, celadon (proto-celadon stoneware) and dark green-glaze porcelain. On exhibition is a tall white porcelain figure of thick paste, partly in black glaze. The use of black glaze in the protruding parts creates a clear-cut outline of the features. It shows that porcelain-making had reached a new level at the time.

## Exhibits

**264 White porcelain figure** of a warrior.
Height 64 cm

**265–272 Painted pottery musicians.** (8 pieces)
Height 17.2 cm-19 cm
Figurines of women playing flute, pan-pipe, **piehli** horn, **pipa** lute and harp, and beating cymbals.

**273 White porcelain figure** of an attendant, partly in black glaze.
Height 71 cm
Greyish white body, covered with yellowish white glaze interspersed with black.

Peasant uprisings toward the end of the Sui dynasty brought in their wake the economic growth of the Tang dynasty and an era of prosperity in the Chinese feudal society. The Tang dynasty was founded in AD 618.

The working people of the Tang dynasty invented the curved-shaft plough. Easy to draw and ploughing deep, it was the most advanced type of its kind at that time. A large number of big and small water conservation projects were carried out in various parts of the country. Improved waterwheels, such as the noria and chain noria, were invented for irrigating the highland. Popularization of new farm implements and expansion of the irrigated area increased grain production. Meanwhile, best traffic along the Grand Canal further promoted economic development in both the north and the south.

The Tang dynasty saw further progress in textiles, paper-making, block-printing and ceramics. The celadon (proto-celadon stoneware) and white porcelain reached a high level of perfection. At the Tungkuanchen kilns at Changsha, Hunan province, copper and iron oxides were used as color agents to produce a brown or green glaze. The world-famous three-colored pottery is a special art work of the Tang dynasty.

The gold and silver work of the Tang dynasty is excellent. Objects with inlaid mother-of-pearl burnished works with gold and silver inlay and other new techniques were also invented.

The Mokao Caves at Tunhuang, Kansu province, are a treasure house of ancient art famous throughout the world. During a thousand years, beginning in Northern Wei, more than a thousand caves were dug into rocky cliffs, most of them being done in the Tang dynasty. They contain many sculptured Buddhist images in beautiful colors. The walls and ceilings of the caves are covered with paintings. The paintings of the Mokao Caves, if joined together, would be 25 kilometers long. They are the immortal works of numerous unknown artists who labored assiduously through the ages.

Frequent economic and cultural interchanges existed between China and other Asian countries in the

Tang dynasty. Products of Chinese applied arts, silks and porcelains were exported in large quantities. Chinese techniques of papermaking, sericulture and silk reeling were introduced to the central and western Asian countries and through the latter to Europe. Chinese working people had also learned handicraft skills from the central and western Asian countries and created art works with their own national characteristics. At Changan, the Tang dynasty capital, many foreigners lived for many years. This helped to promote mutual understanding and cultural interflow between the Chinese and other peoples.

## XXVI Surveys and Excavations of the Tang Capital Changan at Sian, Shensi Province

The Tang dynasty capital of Changan, built in the 7th century AD, was one of the biggest cities of the world at the time. Since the founding of the People's Republic of China extensive surveys have been made at the remaining sites of Changan. Between 1959 and 1960 concerted efforts were made in the excavation of the sites of Hanyuan Hall, Linteh Hall and Hsuanwu Gate, all belonging to the Taming Palace, which yielded remarkable results.

The city walls of Changan were 35.5 kilometers in circumference and the total urban area was 80.89 square kilometers, six times the size of the existing Sian rebuilt in the Ming dynasty. Nearly a million people lived within the city walls. The city of Changan during the Tang dynasty consisted of three main parts: the Imperial Palaces (where the imperial household lived), the Imperial City (the site of the government offices) and the Outer City (the east and the west markets and residential area). The central north-south thoroughfare, Chuchueh Avenue, which was 4.5 kilometers long and 150 meters wide, divided the city into the west and east parts. The remains of the Taming Palace are on the present Lungshou plain north of the city of Sian. Construction of this palace began in AD 634. The Hanyuan Hall was the main hall of the Taming

Palace, and was completed in AD 663. Important court ceremonies were held there, as when the emperor ascended the throne, when officials came to pay homage to the emperor on New Year's Day, etc. The hall itself was 11 **chien** * long, the space between the pillars being 10 meters. It has a floor space of about 2,000 square meters. The Hanyuan Hall was flanked by two symmetrically placed pavilions — one to the west and one to the east. These buildings were connected with covered passages. In front of the palace were broad steps. The Taming Palace is typical of palace structures of the Tang dynasty. Archaeological workers, basing themselves on material already excavated and on historical records, drew restorations which show the magnificence of this Tang dynasty palace.

A hoard of the Tang dynasty was found in 1970 at Hochiatsun village, a southern suburb of Sian. The finds totaled 1,023 pieces. Gold and silver vessels alone accounted for 216 items. In the silver boxes are medicinal minerals — cinnabar, stalacite, etc. There are also instruments for practicing alchemy and making medicines. The hoard was found at the site of the mansion of the Prince of Pin, Li Shou-li, who died in AD 741. Li was a cousin of the emperor Hsuan Tsung. It is possible that some member of his family buried these treasures before fleeing to Szechuan with the emperor and his court when An Lu-shan's troops attacked Changan in the 15th year of Tien Pao (AD 756). In the exhibition are a gold bowl with embossed lotus-flower petals, an octagonal gold cup decorated with human figures, and a silver box with a design of birds and flowers. They are all masterpieces of gold and silver work and reflect the high level of craftsmanship.

### Exhibits

**274 Octagonal gold cup** decorated with human figures.
Height 5.4 cm, major axis 7 cm, minor axis 6.3 cm
On each of the eight faces of the cup is an embossed dancing figure against a floral background. Engraved on the handle is the head of an old man with deep-set eyes, high nose and long beard.

**275 Silver box** with bird and flower design.

Height 6 cm, diameter 13.5 cm

The box is covered with engraved fine interlocking floral design interspersed with small flying birds. Part of it is exquisitely decorated with gold. An ink inscription on the inner surface of the cover reads: "30 **liang** of cinnabar from Kuaichow, 10 **liang** . . . containing gold dust" (with one character illegible) indicates that the box had been used to keep medicine.

**276 Silver bowl** with gilt floral design

Height 3 cm, diameter of mouth 10.1 cm

Engraved with mandarin ducks and scrolls on outer surface and gilt rosette sprays design on inner face, both a background of fish-roe marks.

**277 Silver winged-cup** with gilt floral design.

Height 2.8 cm, major axis 10.5 cm, minor axis 8.6 cm

Wine vessel, engraved with mandarin ducks and water chestnut flower design on outer surface and gilt rosette sprays design on inner face, both on a background of fish-roe marks.

**278 Covered silver bowl** with gilt floral design.

Height 11.4 cm, diameter of mouth 21.9 cm

Engraved floral designs on the belly and surface of the cover, gilded. The ink inscriptions inside the belly and cover read: "2 **jin** and 1 **liang**".

**279 Silver yi** with gilt floral design

Height 8.3 cm

Ewer for pouring water, outside of belly incised with ducks, sashes and pomegranate flowers, gilded. The ink inscription inside reads: "21 **liang**".

**280 Gold bowl** with embossed lotus-petal design.

Height 5.5 cm, diameter of mouth 13.5 cm

The belly is embossed with two rows of upturned lotus-petal design and the whole outer surface again decorated with incised mandarin ducks, parrots, deer, foxes and leaf designs. The bottom of the inner surface of the bowl is incised with rosette sprays

design. Birds and rolling clouds are incised within the foot-rim. Fish-roe marks are used as background for design. Inside there is an ink inscription: "9.3 **liang**".

**281–284 Silver box** containing cinnabar and jade girdle ornaments. (4 items)

Height of box 6.2 cm, diameter of mouth 17 cm

There are "whorl" marks on the box. On both sides of the box-cover are the ink inscriptions: "Bright granulated cinnabar 1 **jin** and 4 **liang**; 15 pieces of pure white jade girdle ornaments with jade buckle missing; a set of Kutu (place name) jade and a set of speckled jade girdle ornaments each consisting of 15 pieces, both complete with jade buckles." Cinnabar is an ingredient for medicine.

**285 & 286 Silver box** containing stalactite. (2 pieces)

Height of box 6.4 cm, diameter of mouth 17 cm

On the box are visible "whorl" marks. The box cover is inscribed in ink on both sides with the characters:

"Second-quality stalactite, 14.3 **liang**. It could be used as medicine." Stalactite is a medicinal substance.

**287 & 288 Silver plate and cinnabar.** (2 pieces)

Height of plate 1.9 cm, diameter of mouth 14.4 cm

Apparent marks of turnery are seen on the silver plate. The fine and close "whorl" marks are concentric, indicating that the plate may have been turned on a simple lathe. Cinnabar is used in medical prescriptions.

**289 & 290 Amber and silver plate.** (2 pieces)

Height of plate 1.9 cm, diameter of mouth 14.3 cm

Amber is an ingredient of medicine.

**291 & 292 Rock crystal and silver plate.** (2 pieces)

Height of plate 1.7 cm, diameter of mouth 18.1 cm

Rock crystal is an ingredient of medicine.

**293 & 294 Amethyst and silver plate.** (2 pieces)

Height of plate 1.7 cm, diameter of mouth 18.7 cm

Also used in medicine.

**295 Silver vessel** in the shape of a pomegranate.

---

* a **chien** is the space between two pillars. It is a Chinese unit of measure for buildings.

Height 8.9 cm. At 1.3 cm below the mouth is a small perforation, the diameter of which is 0.4 cm. The vessel was used for practicing alchemy and preparing medicine.

## Auxiliary Exhibits

F92 City of Changan in Tang Dynasty. (map)
F93 Remains of Hanyuan Hall. (photo)
F94 Plan of the remains of Hanyuan Hall.
F95 Reconstruction of Hanyuan Hall. (drawing)
F96 Remains of Linteh Hall. (photo)
F97 Remains of Hsuanwu Gate. (photo)
F98 Lotus-petal design on gold bowl. (drawing)
F99 Bird and flower design on silver box. (drawing)

## XXVII  Tomb of Princess Yung Tai of Tang Dynasty at Chienhsien, Shensi Province
(AD 706)

In 1962 the tomb of Princess Yung Tai, Li Hsien-hui (AD 685 — 701), was excavated in Chienhsien, Shensi province. Princess Yung Tai was the granddaughter of the famous Empress Wu Tse-tien of the Tang dynasty. She was buried with her prince consort Wu Yen-chi in AD 706. On the surface above the tomb were large stone lions, stone warriors and ornamental pillars, representative of Tang sculpture. The burial accessories inside the tomb totaled more than 1,000 items including three-colored pottery horses, painted pottery figurines and ceramic utensils. The two three-colored pottery horses displayed here are in different poses, one neighing with lifted head and the other grazing with head down. Both are lifelike and in splendid colors. The painted pottery groom with his chest bare is also lifelike and spirited. These are all good specimens of the unique workmanship of the Tang dynasty.

The ceilings and walls of the 87.5-meter passage and the chambers are covered with colored murals. On the princess' stone sarcophagus are incised figures of flowers, birds and palace ladies. The mural of women attendants in the exhibition is distinguished for its lifelike postures and excellent composition.

## Exhibits

**296 Three-colored pottery horse.**
Height 28 cm
With a kaolin base, covered with white and green glaze, decorated with brownish spots. Lead glazed, using low fire, the yellow and brown colors are effected from iron, while the green is from copper.

**297 Yellow glazed pottery horse.**
Height 20.1 cm
With a kaolin base covered all over with yellowish brown glaze.

**298 Three-colored pottery mounted hunter.**
Height 32 cm
The horse is in umber glaze, the rider in green glaze. A hound squats on the horse's back behind the man.

**299 Three-colored pottery mounted hunter.**
Height 31 cm
The horse is in umber glaze, the rider in green robe with black head dress. The hound behind him is missing.

**300 Painted pottery horseman.**
Height 32 cm
The rider in woollen cap is in the gesture of holding the reins. Behind the rider, on the saddle, is a roll-shaped object.

**301 Painted pottery horseman.**
Height 30.5 cm
Mounted on the horse is a bearded man with mouth slightly open, bare to the waist, wearing black boots. He is in the gesture of holding the reins.

**302 Painted pottery mounted hunter.**
Height 31.5 cm
The rider is in black head dress. The horse is painted in red, and on its back is a barking hound.

**303 Three-colored pottery bowl.**

Height 7.4 cm, diameter of mouth 17.2 cm

White porcellaneous base, covered with white glaze and decorated with either green or umber dripped stripes of glaze.

**304 Three-colored pottery dish.**

Height 2.7 cm, diameter of mouth 15 cm

The dish is covered with green glaze on the outer surface while the inner surface is decorated with white and yellow glazed patterns on green ground.

**305 Green glazed pottery bowl.**

Height 8 cm, diameter of mouth 13.7 cm

The bowl is decorated with slightly raised line on the belly.

**306 Women attendants,** wall painting in the tomb of Princess Yung Tai. (copy)

192 cm x 440 cm

The original painting is on the east wall of the antechamber of the tomb. It shows two groups of women attendants. On the left is a group of seven while on the right there are nine, each group with one woman in charge. Behind these are women holding candle-sticks, fans, horse-hair duster, lacquer toilet-boxes and other articles. They are painted in very bright colors and graceful lines, so vividly depicted that one can almost see them with their long gowns sweeping the floor, their hair pertly knotted atop their heads, and some in men's dress. This is a masterpiece of Tang dynasty wall paintings.

**307 & 308 Palace ladies,** incised figures on the stone sarcophagus of Princess Yung Tai. (rubbings)

136 cm x 81 cm

These rubbings of figures of women were taken from engravings on some of the 34 large slabs from which a sarcophagus had been made. The sarcophagus was placed in the rear chamber of the tomb.

## Auxiliary Exhibits

F100 Plan and section of the tomb of Princess Yung Tai.

## XXVIII  Fine and Applied Arts of Tang Dynasty
(AD 618 – 907)

The excavations of Tang dynasty tombs in Shensi, Honan, Kansu and Hunan provinces have yielded large numbers of bronze mirrors, porcelain and three-colored pottery wares. They all show meticulous workmanship. In 1959 a Tang dynasty tomb of the first half of the 8th century was excavated at Chungpao village, Sian. Among the finds are a complete set of building models and sets of three-colored pottery figurines and other articles. The three-colored pottery female figurines deserve particular mention for their lively expressions and resplendent glaze, indicating the high level of plastic art in the Tang dynasty.

In 1971 and 1972 the tombs of the crown princes Chang Huai (AD 654 – 684) and Yi Teh (AD 682 – 701) were unearthed at Chienhsien, Shensi. Crown Prince Chang Huai, Li Hsien, was the second son of Empress Wu Tse-tien. Found in his tomb were more than 600 items of burial objects and over 50 wall paintings. Crown Prince Yi Teh, Li Chung-jun, was grandson of the empress. In his tomb were found more than 1,000 burial objects and over 40 wall paintings. The three-colored pottery horses and wall paintings have high artistic merits, matching those in the tomb of Princess Yung Tai.

## Exhibits

**309 Three-colored pottery horse.**

Early 8th century AD

Height 80 cm, length 82.5 cm

Unearthed in 1971 from the tomb of Crown Prince Yi Teh at Chienhsien, Shensi.

The horse is in yellowish umber glaze, with green saddle blanket, exquisite white and green bridle ornaments and neatly clipped mane with three tufts. Its trace is decorated with bright floral ornaments. It is of large size and a good piece of its kind in Tang dynasty pottery.

**310 & 311 Three-colored pottery pack-camel and groom.** (2 pieces)

8th century AD

Height of groom 29.7 cm, height of camel 47.5 cm, length 40 cm

Unearthed in 1959 at Chungpao village, Sian, Shensi. The groom is in yellow robe. The camel is covered with yellowish brown glaze with flecks of white. The camel's pack contains chickens, rabbits, sheep and silks, demonstrating how in ancient times loaded caravans traveled along the long and exhausting Silk Road.

### 312 & 313 Three-colored pottery horse and groom. (2 pieces)

8th century AD

Height of groom 29 cm, height of horse 40.6 cm, length 42.4 cm

Unearthed in 1959 at Chungpao village, Sian, Shensi. The groom is in light yellow robe and blue shirt, and has a curry-comb at his waist band. The horse is in pale yellow glaze with white mane. Under the saddle is a green blanket.

### 314 & 315 Three-colored pottery figurines of women. (2 pieces)

8th century AD

Height 42 cm and 45 cm

Unearthed in 1959 at Chungpao village, Sian, Shensi. The two figurines are done differently, with yellow, white and blue glaze. Both, however, have powdered faces, rouged lips, and a tinge of ochre on the forehead and false mole at the corner of their mouths. The blue glaze is effected by using cobalt.

### 316 Three-colored pottery warrior.

8th century AD

Height 65.5 cm

Unearthed in 1959 at Chungpao village, Sian, Shensi. The warrior, in armor of blue ground adorned with yellow and white glaze, stands on a pedestal. With open mouth and glaring eyes, he was supposed to guard the tomb against evil spirits.

### 317 Three-colored pottery tomb-guardian.

8th century AD

Height 57.5 cm

Unearthed in 1959 at Chungpao village, Sian, Shensi. This tomb-guardian, with head up and gazing fiercely, has a human head and animal body, with wings on two sides. It is covered with yellow, green, white and blue glaze.

### 318 Yellow glazed pottery ox in lying position.

8th century AD

Length 46 cm

Unearthed in 1965 at Chinan county, Kansu. Covered with yellowish brown glaze.

### 319 Three-colored phoenix-head vase.

8th century AD

Height 32.2 cm

Unearthed in 1961 at Loyang, Honan.

With a flat and globule body, the vase is covered with yellow, green, white and blue glaze and decorated with a phoenix on one side and a mounted archer circled with flower petals on the other.

### 320 Covered pot of three-colored pottery.

8th century AD

Height 21 cm

Unearthed in 1958 at Loyang, Honan.

### 321 White porcelain spittoon.

9th century AD

Height 10.5 cm

Unearthed in 1955 at Sian, Shensi.

White porcellaneous base, covered with clear creamy glaze.

### 322 High-stemmed porcelain bowl with applied floral decoration.

7th century AD

Height 23 cm

Unearthed in 1956 at Sian, Shensi.

Greyish white porcellaneous base, covered with greyish white glaze. The body is decorated variously with appliqué, stampings and engravings.

### 323 Celadon vase with applied design in dark brown.

9th century AD

Height 22.5 cm

Unearthed in 1958 at Changsha, Hunan.
Covered with pale green glaze tinged with yellow. The lower belly is decorated underglaze with splashes of brown. The center of the applied design is marked with the character "Chang" (probably the name of the potter). It represents a new achievement of Tang potters to produce green and brown colors from ferric and copper oxide under the glaze. The discovery of this piece shows that by the Tang dynasty underglaze decorations were already in use.

### 324 Bronze mirror with hunting design.
7th century AD

Diameter 29 cm

Unearthed in 1961 at Fukou, Honan.
The back of the mirror is elegantly decorated with four hunters mounted on horses in chase of animals among mountains and trees. Floral and butterfly designs encircle the scene as a border.

### 325 Bronze mirror with double-phoenix design.
7th century AD

Diameter 23 cm

Unearthed in 1952 at Hsienyang, Shensi.
In the shape of eight flower petals. Around a round knob are phoenixes, scrolls, floral sprays and small flying birds with blossoms in their bills.

### 326 Bronze mirror with bird and animal design.
7th century AD

Diameter 21.5 cm

Unearthed in 1955 at Sian, Shensi.
The knob of the mirror is in the shape of a sea-animal, and around the knob are monsters among interlocking flowers, circled with entwining vines and phoenixes. The entire back is coated with silver foil.

### 327 & 328 Procession scene, wall painting in the tomb of Crown Prince Chang Huai. (2 copies)
Early 8th century AD

150 cm x 240 cm, 148 cm x 204 cm

The original, on the east wall of the tomb passage, depicts some 40 mounted hunters in variously colored short robes, with bows and quivers in their waist bands and either falcons on their forearms or hounds in their arms. In the procession flutter about a dozen colored flags. Vigorous in line, with the hunters lifelike and the animals spirited and agile, the painting successfully depicts the pomp and lavishness of the Tang feudal nobles, and is no doubt one of the masterpieces of Tang paintings.

五
代

Five Dynasties
(AD 907 – 960)

In the year AD 875 the peasant uprising led by Huang Chao (died in AD 884) dealt a mortal blow at the feudal rule of the Tang dynasty. The dynasty fell in AD 907 and the Later Liang dynasty was set up. This was followed in rapid succession by the Later Tang, Later Tsin, Later Han and Later Chou dynasties, all centered in the Yellow River basin. In the same period more than a dozen local powers arose one after another in other parts of the country. Not until AD 960, when the Northern Sung dynasty was founded, did this division of the country that had lasted for more than 50 years end in the main, the period of disunity becoming known in Chinese history as the Five Dynasties.

Improved irrigation in various parts of south China during the Five Dynasties period brought about further development in agricultural and handicraft production. The celebrated Yueh porcelain ware appeared at this time.

## XXIX   Five Dynasties Tomb at Linan, Chekiang Province
(10th century AD)

In 1969, funeral accessories of Wuyueh (AD 893 – 978), a local regime founded during the Five Dynasties period in present-day Chekiang and Kiangsu provinces, were unearthed from a tomb in Linan county, west of Hangchow. Among the finds were a bronze mirror, gold and silver vessels and a score or more of celadon Yueh ware, all of fine texture and workmanship.

Old sites of Yueh kilns have been discovered in Yuyao county of Chekiang province. Since 1957 extensive investigations resulted in the discovery of more than 20 sites where Yueh ware was produced from the Tang to the Northern Sung dynasties. Yueh ware in Tang times was formal in shape and glazed to a soft luster. By the Five Dynasties period this ware was produced in a great variety of forms and types. In addition to incised, carved and applied designs and openwork, painted decorations were also used. The porcelain pot with cloud de-

sign has underglaze painting. The pale green glaze of the bowl is typical of that of Yueh ware in the Five Dynasties period.

## Exhibits

### 329 Porcelain vase with cloud design, Yueh ware.
Height 50.7 cm
Greyish white porcellaneous body with pale green glaze tinged with yellow. On the shoulder and belly of the vase are painted brown lotus-petal and leaf designs.

### 330 Bowl, Yueh ware.
Height 9.5 cm, diameter of mouth 19.9 cm
Greyish white porcellaneous body with pale green glaze.

### 331 Two-handled covered jar, Yueh ware.
Height 19.6 cm
Greyish white porcellaneous body with creamy glaze, lobed body with fluted sides.

### 332 Two-handled kettle-shaped vessel, Yueh ware.
Height 9.2 cm, diameter of mouth 17.6 cm
With pale green glaze on the inner surface. The outer surface is bare.

# 宋 Sung Dynasty
## (AD 960 – 1279)

The Sung dynasty falls into two periods: The Northern Sung (AD 960 – 1127, with its capital at Kaifeng, Honan province) and the Southern Sung (AD 1127 – 1279), with its capital at Linan, the present Hangchow in Chekiang province.

The period of disunity during the Five Dynasties ended with the Northern Sung dynasty. Farming technique was improved. In south China, it was encouraged to raise foxtail millet, wheat, broomcorn millet, beans and other crops commonly grown in north China. Many formerly non-rice-producing areas in north China began to plant paddy. Cotton was grown in Kwangtung and Fukien provinces. With the development of agriculture and handicrafts there arose cities with flourishing commerce. Kaifeng and Linan, capitals of the Northern and Southern Sung dynasties respectively, were populous metropolitan cities where commodities from all over the country were brought and traded. Porcelain-making developed considerably during the Sung dynasty with further developments in the preparation and the firing of body and glaze, as well as in the design and modeling. The Ting and Tzuchow kilns of Hopei, the Ju and Chun kilns of Honan, the Yaochow kilns of Shensi, the Lungchuan kilns of Chekiang and the Chingtehchen kilns of Kiangsi were famous at the time. Their products were noted on the world market as well as at home.

The Sung dynasty was a time when overseas trade and sea communications flourished. Kwangchow, Hangchow, Chuanchow and Mingchow (the present Ningpo in Chekiang province) became important ports for international trade, where commissioners were stationed to take charge and collect revenue. The technique of ship-building made greater progress, and ships with paddle-wheels propelled by men were used in wartime. Large Chinese sea-going vessels carrying five to six hundred passengers plied between China and the Persian Gulf.

The inventions of movable type for printing, the compass and gunpowder are great contributions made to world civilization by the Chinese laboring people during the Sung dynasty.

## XXX Sung Dynasty Porcelain
### (AD 960 – 1279)

1. In 1969, two foundation-deposits were discovered at the bases of two Sung dynasty pagodas in Tinghsien county, Hopei province. One was of the Buddhist Relic Pagoda of Chingchih Monastery rebuilt in AD 977, the 2nd year of the Taiping Hsingkuo (reign mark) in the Sung dynasty. The other was of the Buddhist Relic Pagoda of Chingchung Monastery, built in AD 995, the 1st year of the Chihtao (reign mark) of Sung. A large number of the valuable cultural relics dating from the Northern Wei to the Sung dynasties were unearthed from the deposits, 170 of them being porcelains, mostly white Ting ware dating from early Northern Sung.

A Ting kiln site was discovered at Chuyang in Hopei province. Since the founding of the People's Republic of China, surveys and excavations at key points have been made so that some knowledge has been obtained concerning the development of the Ting ware. Its production began in the 9th century (Later Tang dynasty). White porcelain appeared in the Five Dynasties period (AD 907 – 960). This was generally plain, occasionally decorated with floral designs. In the Northern Sung dynasty (AD 960 – 1127), Ting ware became one of China's famous porcelains. It is mainly white with a smooth, thin body of fine grain. The modeling is excellent and the glaze lustrous and pure. Decorated with carved, incised, or impressed designs. Ting ware ornamentation technique reached a high degree of perfection. The porcelain conch with water pattern on display looks quite like a real conch. The white Ting ware water-pot with incised floral design is tastefully fashioned and of a size rarely seen in this ware.

## Exhibits

**333 Bowl** with lotus flower design, Ting ware.
10th century AD
Height 7.3 cm, diameter of mouth 21.9 cm
Unearthed from the foundation of the Chingchih Monastery pagoda.

The bowl, decorated with carved lotus petals, is supported on a splayed foot and marked on the bottom with the character "Meng" (probably the name of the potter).

**334 Porcelain conch,** Ting ware.

10th century AD

Height 19.8 cm

Unearthed from the foundation of the Chingchih Monastery pagoda.

The conch was used by Buddhist monks as musical instrument during religious services.

**335 Censer** with five feet, Ting ware.

10th century AD

Height 24.1 cm

Unearthed from the foundation of the Chingchih Monastery pagoda.

Incense burner supported on five feet in the shape of human figures. On the cover are seven perforations of different sizes.

**336 Flower-shaped dish** marked with the character "kuan", Ting ware.

10th century AD

Height 3 cm, diameter of mouth 12.8 cm

Unearthed from the foundation of the Chingchih Monastery pagoda.

The center of the dish is decorated with incised confronting cicadas. The bottom is marked with the incised character "kuan" (official) and an ink inscription: "Fifth month of the 2nd year of the Taiping Hsingkuo (reign mark)."

**337 White vase (kendi)** with carved decoration, Ting ware.

10th century AD

Height 60.5 cm

Unearthed from the foundation of the Chingchung Monastery pagoda.

The upper and lower parts of the vase are engraved with lotus-petal design upturned and downward, with engraved interlocking floral designs between.

**338 Flask** incised with floral design, with a silver cover, Ting ware.

10th century AD

Height 19.8 cm

Unearthed from the foundation of the Chingchung Monastery pagoda.

With a gilded silver cover and foot-rim. The flask shoulder and belly are decorated with engraved upturned lotus-petal design.

2. The Lungchuan kilns were located in Lungchuan county, Chekiang province. Systematic surveys and excavations at key points of the Lungchuan kilns began in 1956, and 200 or more Lungchuan kiln ruins have been discovered. The Lungchuan kilns, based on the Yueh, date from the Five Dynasties period. They underwent further development in the Northern Sung dynasty. Varieties of shapes of vessels increased. Cloud, plantain-leaf, fish and lotus-petal designs came into vogue, the color of the glaze being pale green with a tinge of greyish yellow. During the Southern Sung period, when Lungchuan ware was at its best, there were two main types: white-bodied celadons and black-bodied celadons. The former are symmetrically and evenly moulded and varied in form. The designs were usually done in relief or appliqué. The glaze is thick, smooth and mellow, with delightful plum green and powder green (light greenish blue) glazes. The black-bodied celadons are of a fine, close texture. The body in grey-black was known as "iron bone". The glaze is often crackled, some in a wide network, others in close patterns of small crackles over the outer surface. Their unglazed foot-rim and thinly glazed mouth-rim appear in dark brown as a result of re-oxidation, and the ware is described as having "purple rim and iron feet". After the Yuan and then the Ming dynasties, Lungchuan ware yielded place to Chingtehchen. The pieces on display are representative of Sung dynasty Lungchuan ware unearthed in various parts of Chekiang province.

## Exhibits

**339 Vase** decorated with dragon design. Lungchuan ware.

12th century AD

Height 19 cm

Unearthed in 1956 at Tayao, Lungchuan county, Chekiang.

Greyish white porcellaneous body with pale green glaze. The body of the vase is vertically gadrooned. Its shoulder is decorated with a coiled dragon.

**340 Bowl** with lotus-petal design, Lungchuan ware.
Early 13th century AD
Height 6.5 cm, diameter of mouth 13.5 cm
Unearthed in 1960 at Lungchuan county, Chekiang.
With light greenish blue glaze on both outer and inner surfaces, it is as mellow as jade.

**341 Water-dropper** in the shape of a boat, Lungchuan ware.
12th century AD
Length 17.3 cm
Unearthed in 1956 at Lungchuan, Chekiang.
Water-dropper used in preparing ink on an inkstone, greyish white body with bluish green glaze. Two figures can be seen sitting inside the cabin of the boat.

**342 Tripod censer,** Lungchuan ware.
Early 13th century AD
Height 12.4 cm
Unearthed in 1954 at Juian county, Chekiang.
Plum green glaze.

3. **Ying-ching** misty blue ware was a new creation at the Chingtehchen kilns during the Sung dynasty. It is thin-walled, of fine texture, symmetrically and elegantly fashioned, and glazed in pure and lustrous white with a tinge of blue. The color varies, since the glaze is thicker in the impressed lines, producing a "hidden pattern" as on silk. The **ying-ching** bowl on display, decorated with incised floral design, is glazed to a bluish white and is fresh and light in appearance. The wine pot with a warmer on exhibition is also a fine specimen of **ying-ching** porcelain of the Sung dynasty.

The Yaochow kilns, the ruins of which were discovered only after the founding of the People's Republic of China, were located at Tungchuan in Shensi province. The products made during the Northern Sung period are of high quality, being thin-walled and pure-glazed.

The Tzuchow kiln sites are at Tzuhsien in Hopei province. They were folk kilns whose products featured designs over a white background, mainly in realistic style. The head-rest on exhibition is decorated in the style of folk art and depicts a boy fishing. This is a typical specimen of Tzuchow ware.

Exhibits

**343 Ying-ching** wine pot with warmer.
11th century AD
Height of pot 25.8 cm, height of warmer 14 cm
Unearthed in 1963 at Susung, Anhwei.
White body with bluish white glaze. The pot and the lotus-petal shaped warmer make a set. The form is exquisite, the glaze pure.

**344 Ying-ching bowl.**
13th century AD
Height 9.8 cm, diameter 21.2 cm
Unearthed in 1965 at Tehan, Kiangsi.
The bowl is covered with greenish white glaze tinged with yellow, very pure and bright.

**345 Ying-ching bowl** incised with floral design.
12th century AD
Height 7.2 cm, diameter of mouth 20.5 cm
Unearthed in 1952 at Nanchang, Kiangsi.
Thinly bodied and covered with greenish white glaze, the bowl appears translucent. On inner surface is incised scroll design.

**346 Tripod censer,** Yaochow ware.
13th century AD
Height 27 cm
Unearthed in 1960 at Lantian, Shensi.
Pale green glaze tinged with yellow, decorated on the belly with six groups of appliqué designs.

**347 Pillow** with fishing design, Tzuchow ware.
12th century AD
Length 28.8 cm

Unearthed in 1955 at Hsingtai, Hopei.

Painted on the surface of the pillow is a boy fishing. The reverse side is stamped with the characters: "Chang Chia Chen" (pillow made for the Chang Family). The method of decoration on Tzuchow ware paved the way for later blue-and-white and polychrome porcelains of the Yuan and Ming dynasties.

## Auxiliary Exhibits

F101 Underground foundation-deposit of a Sung pagoda at Tinghsien. (photo)

F102 Remains of a Lungchuan kiln. (photo)

The Liao dynasty was founded in northern China by the Khitans, one of the nationalities of China at that time. In very early times the Khitan people lived along the Shalamulun River, the upper reaches of the Liao River. During the early Tang dynasty, a Sungmo Prefecture was instituted to govern the area. In the year AD 916 the various Khitan tribes were united and founded their own kingdom with its capital at Linhuang (their Upper Capital, in the vicinity of today's Barin Left Banner of Liaoning province). In AD 947 the kingdom was renamed Liao; it was subjugated by the Kin dynasty in AD 1125.

The Kin dynasty was founded in northeastern China by the Nuchens, one of the nationalities of China at that time. The Nuchens were descended from the Mohe tribes in the Heishui region in northeastern China and lived along the Sunghua River and the lower reaches of the Heilung River. During the early Tang dynasty, a Heishui Prefecture was instituted. The Nuchen tribes were united at the beginning of the 12th century. In AD 1115 the Nuchens founded the Kin dynasty with their capital at Huining (south of present-day Acheng in Heilungkiang province). It was subjugated by the Mongols in AD 1234.

During the period in which the Sung, Liao and Kin dynasties existed side by side in China there was frequent economic and cultural interflow among the different nationalities, who jointly created this period in China's history as a multi-national country.

At the end of the 12th century the Mongolian tribes inhabiting the region between the Khingan and the Altai mountains became united and founded the Yuan dynasty in AD 1271, with its capital in Tatu (present-day Peking). The subjugation of Kin and Southern Sung by the Yuan dynasty ended the period of disunity in China. This resulted in the expansion of economic links between various parts of China and the further consolidation of a unified, feudal, multinational country.

In AD 1289 the laboring people of various nationalities dredged the Grand Canal. They also dug the

Huitung Canal in Shantung province and the Tunghui Canal in Hopei, so that the Grand Canal was extended further north passing through Shantung. Boats from the south with their cargoes were then able to come directly into the city area of the capital, Tatu.

Handicraft industry and commerce developed considerably during the Yuan dynasty, giving fresh impetus to overseas trade. The noted blue-and-white and underglazed red porcelains represented new techniques in Chinese ceramics. The blue-and-white porcelains of the Yuan dynasty were exquisitely done and demonstrated the outstanding skill of craftsmanship at that period. They found markets in Africa and other distant lands. In the early years of the Yuan dynasty the Venetian Marco Polo (AD 1254 – 1324) toured various major cities of China. His **Travels** gives the West a concrete and vivid picture of China's prosperity and strength at that time.

## XXXI Tomb of a Liao Princess' Consort at Chihfeng, Liaoning Province
(AD 959)

In 1953 the tomb of Prince Wei Kuo, consort of a Liao princess, was discovered at Chihfeng in Liaoning province. He was interred in AD 959. The tomb contained more than 2,000 funeral accessories, most of them used during the lifetime of the prince. Among the objects were sets of riding equipment ornamented with various splendid designs like acanthus, entwining plants, flying phoenix and coiling dragon—all traditional Han designs during the Tang and Five Dynasties periods. White porcelains form the major proportion of the porcelain wares unearthed. The white porcelain plate marked with the Han character "kuan" (official) is in the traditional Han style, while the white porcelain flask ornamented with a cockscomb bears special features of the Khitans.

Exhibits

**348 White porcelain plate** marked with the character "kuan".
Height 5.4 cm, diameter of mouth 22.3 cm
The mouth-rim is inlaid with a gilt silver border; on the bottom is incised the character "kuan" (official).

**349 White porcelain flat flask** ornamented with a cockscomb.
Height 23.5 cm
The shape of the flask was developed from the leather pouch used by the Khitan nationality at that time in north China. The body of the flask is flat, with the top in cockscomb shape. At both sides and below the belly are "seams" in imitation of the stitching on the leather pouch.

**350 & 351 Iron heads of whistling arrows.** (2 pieces)
Length 10 cm & 9.5 cm
The whistle is made of bone, with four small perforations at the center, so that it gave a signal by whistling. The tip is equipped with a double-barb iron arrow head with a stem for attaching the arrow head to the arrow shaft.

**352 & 353 Gilt silver saddle ornaments.** (2 pieces)
Height 27.7 cm & 37.5 cm
These silver ornaments are used to decorate the pommel and cantle (or hind bow) of saddle. Made of gilt silver, they are embossed with a pair of dragons frolicking with a pearl in the waves.

**354 Silver cup with stand.**
Height 8.5 cm, diameter of stand 16 cm
The cup is of a piece with its stemmed stand, both being embossed all over with a floral design.

**355 Gilt silver tassel ornament for horse.**
Height 6 cm, diameter 19.2 cm
This gilt silver ornament, which was meant to be suspended from a horse's neck, resembles a bowl turned upside down with a floral shaped mouth-rim. It is decorated with embossed double-phoenix and

scroll designs. There is a small hole in the center for attaching the tassel.

## Auxiliary Exhibits

F103 The tomb of Prince Wei Kuo, consort of a Liao princess, at Chihfeng. (plan and section)
F104 Restoration of iron heads of whistling arrows. (drawing)

## XXXII  Pottery Dramatic Actors of the Kin and Yuan Dynasties from Shansi and Honan Provinces
### (AD 1115 – 1368)

Chinese drama has an early origin. During the Tang period, song and dance items and balladry were already popular. By the Sung dynasty, there appeared in Kaifeng an early form of theater, with a square stage on level ground enclosed in railings where dramas were performed. The Yuan period was a time when drama flourished. A composite art was created of music, song and dance, recitation and acting with well-developed plots. Performances were at fixed theaters, with woman and man actors.

Since the founding of the People's Republic of China, several remains of a Yuan dynasty theater have been found in Shansi. Models of stage shows and figurines of actors were also found in brick-lined tombs of the Kin and Yuan dynasties, showing the extent of the development of drama at that time. The stage depicted on carved brick from a Kin tomb on exhibit demonstrates the existence of theater structures of brick and wood at that time. The Kin and Yuan actors are portrayed in a life-like manner in pottery figures. A Yuan dynasty wall painting also depicts a dramatic performance of that period.

## Exhibits

**356–358 Pottery actors.** (3 pieces)
13th century AD (Kin)
Height 19.5 cm-21 cm
Unearthed in 1965 at Houma, Shansi.
Mould-made grey pottery figurines.

**359–361 Pottery actors and dancers.** (3 pieces)
14th century AD (Yuan)
Height 37 cm-39.2 cm
Unearthed in 1963 at Chiaotso, Honan.
Grey pottery. One is dancing, one whistling, and one stepping sidewise with clappers in hand.

## Auxiliary Exhibits

F105 A stage depicted on carved brick from a Kin tomb at Houma, Shansi. (photo)

F106 Yuan dynasty wall painting depicting a dramatic performance, from a temple at Hungtung, Shansi. (copy reduced in size)

## XXXIII  Remains of the Yuan Capital, Tatu, at Peking
### (AD 1267 – 1368)

The Yuan capital, Tatu, the construction of which began in AD 1267, was located in present-day Peking, capital of the People's Republic of China. Tatu was one of the famous world metropolises at that time, with a circumference of 28.6 kilometers and an area of 50 square kilometers.

Since the founding of the People's Republic of China, extensive surveys and selective excavations have been carried out. They have greatly added to our knowledge concerning the general layout and history of this Yuan capital. During the Great Proletarian Cultural Revolution, when remains of the barbican entrance of Ho Yi Gate and several dwellings were unearthed, a large number of porcelains and parts of sculpture and reliefs for architectural purposes were uncovered.

The barbican outside the city gate of the Yuan capital, Tatu, was built in AD 1358 by the Yuan rulers, who feared peasant uprisings. It was equipped with fire-extinguishing apparatus against attack by fire. However, within ten years the Yuan feudal rule crumbled under the powerful onslaughts of the uprising peasants.

## Exhibits

**362 Ying-ching statuette of Kuanyin**
First half of 14th century AD
Height 66 cm
Unearthed in 1955 in the west city of Peking.
A diadem on her head, jewelled necklaces and strings of ornaments draped over her robes, the statuette is of white porcelain body covered with pale green glaze. Both in form and glaze color it is most exquisite, a fine specimen among the ying-ching porcelain statuettes from the Yuan dynasty.

**363 Openwork censer of three-colored glazed pottery.**
End of 13th century AD
Height 36 cm
Unearthed in 1964 in the Haitien district of Peking.
Covered with glaze in blue, green and yellow, the body of the censer has openwork designs of dragon, phoenix, and peonies. The mountain-shaped lid is decorated with a coiled dragon.

**364 Blue-and-white covered jar with floral design.**
First half of 14th century AD
Height 66 cm
Unearthed in 1961 in the Haitien district of Peking.
With ovoid body and shallow lobes, the vessel has an underglazed red lid moulded in the form of lotus leaf, the lid and body being painted with 17 bands of designs consisting of flowers of various kinds. It is neat in form, with clear-cut decorative patterns.

**365 Blue-and-white porcelain vase.**
First half of 14th century AD
Height 15.3 cm

Unearthed in 1962 in the west city of Peking. White body with sandy bottom. The shape is that of the bronze **ku** (wine vessel) of ancient times. Inside the everted mouth-rim are scroll patterns.

**366 Plate, Chun ware.**
First half of 14th century AD
Height 4.5 cm, diameter of mouth 22.3 cm
Unearthed in 1969 at Fangshan, Peking.
Covered with sky-blue glaze, its center has purple spots.

**367 Ying-ching brush-rest.**
First half of 14th century AD
Length 18 cm
Unearthed in 1962 in the west city of Peking.
Pale green glaze. Its openwork forms five mountain peaks, with the sun over the central peak and cloud overhanging the others. Lower down on the mountains are entwining vines, while the base is decorated with surging waves.

**368 Porcelain jar** decorated with two phoenixes in black on white ground.
13th century AD
Height 36 cm
Unearthed in 1970 at Fangshan, Peking.
White glaze. Its shoulder is painted with stylized lotus-petal and chrysanthemum designs, and the belly with two phoenixes in flight among clouds.

## Auxiliary Exhibits

F107 Tatu, capital of the Yuan dynasty. (plan)

F108 Northern part of the city wall of Tatu. (photo)

F109 Barbican entrance to Ho Yi Gate. (photo)

F110 Remains of Houyingfang Residence. (photo)

F111 Site of Houyingfang Residence during excavation. (photo)

F112 Reconstruction of Houyingfang Residence. (drawing)

## XXXIV Porcelain, Silver and Lacquer Wares of the Yuan Dynasty
(AD 1271 – 1368)

The porcelain, silver and lacquer wares of the Yuan period, patterned on the traditional style of the past, show further improvement in workmanship. The blue color in the blue-and-white porcelain is cobalt oxide painted under the glaze. Blue-and-white porcelain probably made its first appearance in the late Southern Sung dynasty, though the technique at that time was crude. By the Yuan period there had been great technical development in Chingtehchen ware, so there could be produced generally such fine blue-and-white porcelain. The pot with lid decorated with white dragon design exhibited here is a rare specimen of Yuan dynasty blue-and-white porcelain.

Chun ware was produced at Yuhsien in Honan. This ware is known worldwide for its rose-purple and begonia-red glazes, like the colors of clouds at dawn. Silver objects from the Yuan period unearthed in Anhwei and Kiangsu provinces are beautifully executed, of pleasing shape and lively design. The exhibits here are only a part of the objects unearthed.

## Exhibits

**369 Blue-and-white covered pot** decorated with white dragon design.
First half of 14th century AD
Height 51.5 cm
Unearthed in 1964 at Paoting, Hopei.
The lid has a lion-shaped knob. The octagonal body is painted with a blue-and-white wave pattern which brings out the four white frolicking dragons in relief.

**370 Blue-and-white ewer** with floral design.
First half of 14th century AD
Height 26.5 cm
Unearthed in 1964 at Paoting, Hopei.
Octagonal shaped, it is modeled after such vessels made of gold and silver.

**371 Basin,** Chun ware.
13th century AD
Height 10.6 cm, diameter of mouth 44 cm
Unearthed in 1955 at Paoting, Hopei.
Covered with sky-blue glaze and decked with nine rose-purple spots inside and outside.

**372 Silver confectionery box** decorated with double phoenix pattern.
First half of 14th century AD
Height 15.9 cm, diameter 35 cm
Unearthed in 1955 at Hofei, Anhwei.
The surface of the cover is incised with two phoenixes among flowers, the body of the box with scrolls and flowers.
figures.

**373 Round box of lacquerware** carved with human figures.
First half of 14th century AD
Height 3.9 cm, diameter 12.1 cm
Crimson, the surface of the cover carved with a scene depicting the celebrated poet Tao Chien (AD 365 – 427) gathering chrysanthemums by the eastern fence. It was found in 1953 from the tomb of Jen Jen-fa (AD 1254 – 1327) at Chingpu, Shanghai. Jen Jen-fa was a well-known Yuan dynasty painter who specialized in drawing horses and human figures as well as flowers and birds.

**374–385 Toilet articles and silver toilet box with stand. (12 pieces)**
14th century AD
Height of box 24.3 cm, diameter 17 cm, height of mirror-stand 30.4 cm
Unearthed in 1964 at Soochow, Kiangsu.
The toilet box consists of three tiers. The surface of its cover and body is engraved with tree-peony, yellow jasmine and rose mallow designs. This box originally contained 18 silver toilet articles. Ten of these on display include 2 pots, 2 boxes, a pair of scissors, 2 brushes, 2 combs and a mirror. The toilet box is placed on a tray. The mirror-stand is in the form of a folding chair, the back of which,

engraved with a moon and rabbit and in slanting position, serves as the mirror support. The surface of the mirror base is decorated with a double phoenix and hundred flower design and scroll patterns.

## Auxiliary Exhibit

F113 Design on the silver confectionery box decorated with two phoenixes.

## Auxiliary Exhibits

F114 The Great Wall. (photo)

F115 Partial view of the Mokao Caves at Tunhuang, Kansu. (photo)

F116 Hall of Prayer for Good Harvests of the Temple of Heaven in Peking. (photo)

F117 Stone sculpture of Fenghsien Temple at Lungmen, Loyang. (photo)

F118 Masses visiting the Exhibition of Cultural Relics Unearthed During the Great Proletarian Cultural Revolution. (photo)

F119 Books and periodicals on archaeology and the study of cultural relics published in the People's Republic of China.